DOLPH

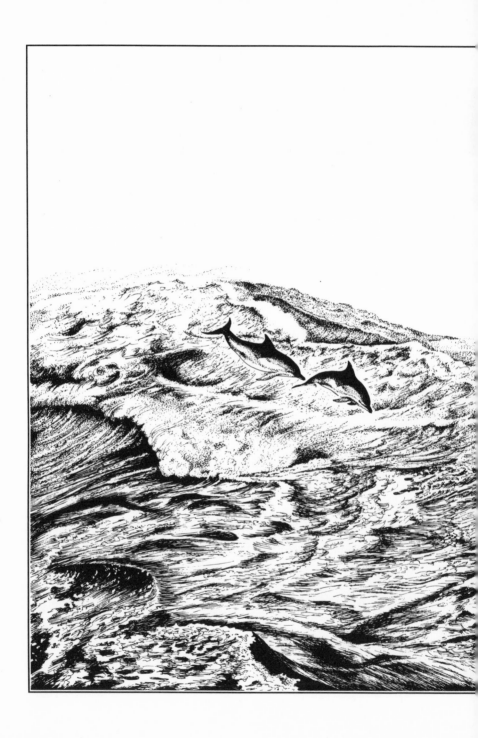

DOLPHINS

Peter Evans

with illustrations by

EUAN DUNN

Whittet Books

TITLE PAGE ILLUSTRATION: *Common dolphins in a rough sea.*

First published 1994
Text © 1994 by Peter Evans
Illustrations © 1994 by Euan Dunn
Whittet Books Ltd, 18 Anley Road, London W14 OBY

British Library Cataloguing in Publication Data
A catalogue record for this book is available from the British Library

ISBN 1 873580 13 4

Printed and bound by WBC, Bridgend, Mid Glam.

Contents

Acknowledgments

First I should like to thank my parents for helping me develop my early interest in dolphins, with further help and encouragement from Pete Kinnear to found the UK Cetacean Group, and to Sidney Brown and Ray Gambell (then of the Whale Research Unit), Peter Purves (of the British Natural History Museum), and Paul Racey (of Aberdeen University). I owe them all a great debt. With the development of the Cetacean Group, I received willing help from Stephan Harding, Stephanie Hall, Mary-Rose Lane, Gina Scanlan, Annabel Seddon, Glen Tyler, Juliet Vickery and Viv Wood, and more recently, from Lucy Gilbert, Rachel Harding-Hill, Emily Lewis and Mike Lewis. In addition, the network of enthusiastic volunteer observers, now numbering over a thousand, has contributed greatly to our basic knowledge of the status and distribution of dolphins in British and Irish waters.

Others who have contributed in important ways over the years include Euan Dunn, Hugo Mony-Coutts, Caroline Crawford, Pete Ewins, Martin Heubeck, Peter Hope-Jones, Mike Richardson, Mark Tasker and Hugh Watson, whilst funding support has come at various times from the UK Department of the Environment, Nature Conservancy Council, Worldwide Fund for Nature, British Ecological Society, Greenpeace, the Whale and Dolphin Conservation Society and Glenmorangie.

I have been very lucky to have the informed artistic talents of Euan Dunn to brighten up the text. His guidance has also been a great help in the presentation of this book. Finally, I thank Annabel Whittet for her supporting role as sympathetic editor.

Preface

My earliest memory of a dolphin was probably similar to that of many other people's — a splash half a mile offshore from a busy holiday resort, a shower of spray in a September sun, and the torpedo-shaped body of a bottle-nosed dolphin lurching into the air in probable pursuit of a salmon or sea trout. For most, this is virtually the only glimpse they will have into the mysterious lives of the dolphins that rule our seas. For a few thousand years we have paid reverence to their grace and beauty, often giving them mythological powers. And yet, over the same period, we have hunted them for meat, trapped them in our nets either intentionally or by accident, or driven them away by damaging their local environment.

In recent years, public attention has centred upon the demise of the great whales after relentless over-exploitation. The result of this was that for a long time many environmental groups overlooked the problems that dolphins had been facing, particularly over the last half century. The last decade has seen a welcome awakening of awareness and concern for these small cousins of the great whales.

In this book, I have tried to summarize in a manner that is accessible to the general reader our current knowledge of dolphins in the world's seas and rivers. I have placed emphasis upon the recent advances we have made and review the major threats that dolphins face at this present time. As with the companion volume on *Whales*, the book is not exhaustive, and I have included a list of recommended books at the end, for those who seek more detailed information.

The order of mammals called *Cetacea* (from the Greek *ketos* and the Latin *cetu* , both meaning 'whale') includes all whales, dolphins and porpoises. Thes are subdivided into two main living groups, the Mysticeti ('moustached' or baleen whales) and the Odontoceti (or 'toothed' whales, which includes also all the dolphins and porpoises), the division being based upon the way we believe the different groups evolved. In a previous book (*Whales* in the same series), I reviewed all members of the Mysticeti, and the larger whales amongst the Odontoceti — the sperm whale (and its two smaller relatives), and all the beaked whales. In this book, I shall consider all other members of the Odontoceti. Most of these are true dolphins, but all other small cetaceans such as porpoises, pilot whales and killer whales, will also be treated. Because of their evolutionary relationship to one another, they are commonly referred to collectively as 'Dolphins'.

Dr Peter Evans
Department of Zoology, University of Oxford 1993

Hourglass dolphins

•1•

Dolphin Origins and Diversity

If people over the centuries have repeatedly mistaken whales for fish, then it should come as no surprise that many still confuse dolphins with sharks. Both have a back fin, are of similar torpedo shape, and frequently swim near the surface. However, that is as far as the comparison goes. Being mammalian, dolphins are warm-blooded, and they breathe air with lungs so that they must periodically come to the surface. They give birth to live young which the mother suckles on milk secreted by its mammary glands. Sharks and other fish are cold-blooded, and, with oxygen in their tissues, they do not need to make regular forays to the surface to breathe. Most fish either lay eggs or give birth to independently feeding young.

The ancestors of the cetaceans are thought to have been primitive ungulates, large bodied creatures living in the Paleocene epoch (65 to 54 million years ago); their fossils have been found in the sediments of estuaries and lagoons which suggests that some were moving towards an aquatic existence (though they still had four legs). The Eocene epoch (50 million years ago) saw the rise of the mammals as a group and their division into many species which filled niches previously occupied by the great reptiles. Much of Europe was subsiding after a period of major mountain building and volcanic activity and this caused shallow continental seas to advance westward into what is now Western Asia, North Africa and the Mediterranean. Here lived the first recognizable ancestors of whales and dolphins, which have been classified as a separate suborder Archaeoceti; although they do not seem to have been direct ancestors of today's cetaceans, they did have some similarities: their bodies were elongated into torpedo shapes, with short necks and long tails. Their hindlimbs were reduced, and their forelimbs were paddle shaped. They had long palates and their nostrils had migrated to the top of the head. Also, in contrast to fish, whose tails move sideways, the tails of Archaeocetes moved up and down (as do present day dolphins' tails).

Most palaeontologists nowadays believe that both the Mysticeti (baleen or whalebone whales) and the Odontoceti (toothed whales, including all dolphins) have a common ancestry; the Mysticeti evolved from a toothed ancestor some time in the Oligocene epoch (39 to 25 million years ago) and during this time other families of cetaceans appear to have evolved.

The progressively more aquatic way of life experienced by all the cetacean families resulted in a backwards shift of the external nostrils so that they could be readily placed above the water, and the development of structures to seal them against water during dives. The long mobile neck, functional hindlimbs and, eventually, most of the pelvic girdle were all lost, together with any external coat of hair that their terrestrial ancestors might have had. At the same time, the body was becoming more torpedo-shaped for greater streamlining through the water, and a dorsal fin developed

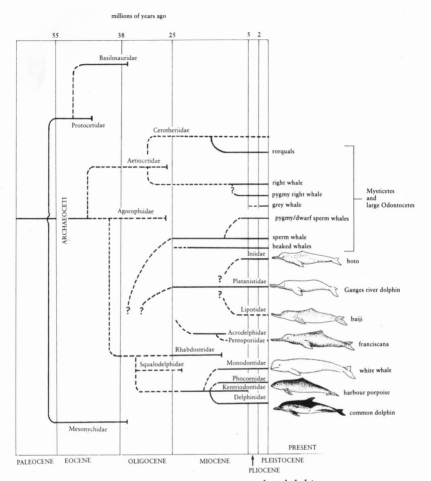

millions of years ago

55   38   25   5   2

Basilosauridae

Protocetidae

Cetotheriidae

rorquals

Aetiocetidae

right whale
pygmy right whale
grey whale

Mysticetes
and
large Odontocetes

Agorophiidae

pygmy/dwarf sperm whales

sperm whale
beaked whales

ARCHAEOCETI

Iniidae   boto

Platanistidae   Ganges river dolphin

Lipotidae   baiji

Acrodelphidae
Pentoporiidae   franciscana

Rhabdosteidae

Squalodelphidae   Monodontidae   white whale

Phocoenidae
Kentriodontidae   harbour porpoise
Delphinidae

common dolphin

Mesonychidae

PRESENT

PALEOCENE   EOCENE   OLIGOCENE   MIOCENE   PLEISTOCENE
                                             PLIOCENE

Evolutionary route to present-day dolphins

for stability together with horizontal tail flukes for forward propulsion.

The most primitive Odontocetes (like the Archaeocetes before them) had 'heterodont' dentition. This means that the teeth were differentiated into different types (for example long, pointed teeth at the front and broader cheek teeth). However, during the Late Oligocene, the teeth became modified in some groups to form the long rows of many sharp uniform teeth with single roots and conical crowns typical of a number of the present-day Odontocetes.

The earliest true Odontocetes were short-beaked whales with triangular shark-like teeth (members of the family Agorophiidae). These gave rise to the squalodonts which are thought to have been most abundant in the late

Oligocene and early Miocene, 20-25 million years ago. The squalodonts were relatively large animals, three metres or more in length, with skulls which had by now become almost fully telescoped with nostrils on the top of the head. They had many teeth which remained differentiated. During the Miocene, they gave rise to a family of very long-snouted dolphins, generally referred to as the Rhabdosteidae. Most were about 3 metres in length and, judging by the quantity of fossils found all over the world (from Europe and North Amertica to Australia and South America), they must have been very abundant and widely distributed. Although they had fully telescoped skulls, and many similar-shaped (termed homodont) teeth, they had symmetrically shaped skulls in contrast to modern delphinids. By the Middle Miocene, about 15 million years ago, they were probably being superseded by representatives of families with relatives living to this day.

Within the Odontocetes, the largest number of species fall into the superfamily Delphinoidea. Living groups include the Delphinidae (true dolphins), Phocoenidae (porpoises) and Monodontidae (white whales and narwhals).

DELPHINIDAE— true dolphins

The family Delphinidae is a relatively modern group, the oldest known fossil coming from the Late Miocene (about 11 million years ago). Most fossils that have been found come from Pliocene deposits in Europe, but owing to the generally oceanic habit of members of this family, they are not as abundant as might be expected from such a successful and diverse family. They appear to have had quite generalized diets, and intermediate-sized beaks. Most living members have functional teeth in both jaws, a fat-filled forehead termed the melon, with a distinct beak, and a dorsal fin. Unlike their ancestors, they possess a markedly asymmetrically shaped skull with a single crescent-shaped blowhole, the concave side of which faces forward on top of the head. There are at least 31 members of the family, ranging in size from the 2 metre (6 feet) long common, striped (or euphrosyne), and spinner dolphins through to the 6-8 metre (18-25 feet) long killer whale and slightly smaller long-finned and short-finned pilot whales. Within this large and disparate family are several groupings of closely related species each occupying a particular ocean or climatic region. For example, there is a hump-backed dolphin living in the Atlantic off the coasts of West Africa, and a counterpart in the Indo-Pacific; a white-sided dolphin in the North Atlantic and another in the North Pacific; a northern right whale dolphin confined to temperate waters of the North Pacific and a southern right whale dolphin in the Southern Ocean. We assume that such pairs of species have a common ancestor whose populations became split when regions of sea with favourable conditions became more distant from one another.

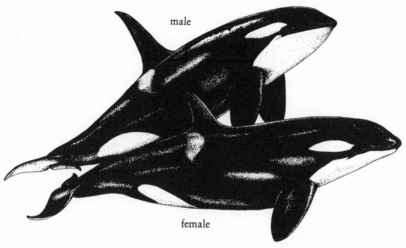

male

female

Killer whales.

PHOCOENIDAE— porpoises

The families Phocoenidae and Monodontidae are now recognized as separate from the Delphinidae. The earliest members also date from the Late Miocene. Fossil phocoenids have been found along the Pacific coasts of North and South America, suggesting that they originated in the shallow waters that occupied temperate latitudes of the North Pacific at that time. Living members of the Phocoenidae form a rather uniform group. They are all small (about 1.2-2.1 metres/4-7 feet in length), with a rounded foreheads and no beaks. All except for the **finless porpoise** of South-East Asia have small, low triangular dorsal fins, centrally placed on the back. The many teeth are spade-like in shape, flattened and laterally compressed when compared with the teeth of the true delphinids. The skull also differs in having a protrusion on each jawbone in front of the opening to the external nostrils or nares. There are six living representatives of this family. The most familiar to people living on the shores of the North Atlantic and North Pacific is the **harbour porpoise,** which occurs mainly in temperate and subarctic coastal seas. Also in the North Pacific live various forms (differentiated by colour pattern) of **Dall's porpoise,** and from China south and west into the Indian Ocean, the **finless porpoise.** The rarest of all porpoises is the **vaquita** which is confined to the Gulf of California, Mexico, and is considered seriously endangered. In the Southern Oceans, the counterparts are the **Burmeister's porpoise** and the **spectacled porpoise,** both from coastal waters of temperate South America south to the Falkland Islands.

Harbour porpoise.

MONODONTIDAE— beluga, narwhal and Irrawaddy dolphin

The family Monodontidae includes three living members — the **white whale** or **beluga,** and the **narwhal,** both confined to the Arctic; and the **Irrawaddy dolphin** of the Indo-Pacific, which until recently was thought to belong to the family Delphinidae. The **narwhal** and **white whale** both lack a dorsal fin, and their flippers turn upwards at the tips as they get older. The narwhal has only two teeth, neither of which actually function as teeth. These are short in the female, but in the male the left tooth continues to grow to form an elongated tusk. The **white whale,** on the other hand, has between 8 and 11 teeth in each jaw, and these are often curved and irregular in form. Although possessing a small sickle-shaped dorsal fin, the **Irrawaddy dolphin** has a similar shaped stout body with rounded snout and no beak, and broad, fairly long paddle-like flippers. It has between 12 and 19 pairs of small conical teeth in each jaw. The fossil record indicates that monodonts once also occupied temperate seas as far south as Baja California in the North-East Pacific, during the Late Miocene and Pliocene.

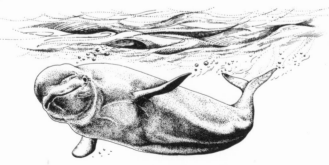

Beluga.

DOLPHINS IN DANGER — THE RIVER DOLPHINS

In some of the greatest rivers of the world, dolphins have returned from a marine existence to live in freshwater. One species, the **franciscana**, remains in a broadly estuarine or coastal marine environment, occurring in the estuary of La Plata river and along the coastlines of Brazil and eastern Argentina. Other species live in the Amazon and Orinoco in Central and South America, the Indus of Sind and Punjab in Pakistan, and the Ganges, Brahmaputra, Kharnaphuli and Meghna river systems of western India, and finally in the Yangtze river in China. Living in often turbid water, the river dolphins tend to have much reduced eyesight, relying upon echolocation to find their way about and locate prey, and on their sense of touch. Several of the species frequently swim on their sides, possibly using the leading edge of the flipper to probe the bottom for fish, shrimps or molluscs upon which they mainly feed, or to help navigation.

Throughout the world, river dolphins are in trouble, facing a variety of threats as humans disturb, develop and degrade their habitats. The most endangered of all is the **baiji** with somewhere around three hundred individuals remaining, confined to the Yangtze river. Significant numbers have died as a result of entanglement in longline fishing nets set on the river bottom, whilst collisions with vessels along the lower reaches of the river continue to be a problem. Additionally, the construction of dams and other barriers along the river and its tributaries has led to changes in fish abundance and distribution, and overfishing has further reduced their numbers. In an attempt to save the species from extinction, the Chinese Government has given the species full protection status, establishing one natural protection area (from Loushan to Xin Tankou in Hubei Province) and proposing two other semi-natural reserves (at Tongling on the lower Yangtze and Shi Shou in Hubei Province on the middle Yangtze). Recent field studies have shown recognizable individuals travel over 125 miles (200 kilometres) downstream, indicating a much larger range than previously thought.

Two other river dolphins may be found in Asia — the **Ganges susu** or **Ganges river dolphin** and the **Indus susu** or **Indus river dolphin** occupying those respective river systems. The habitat of the Ganges susu is being severely degraded throughout India, Bangladesh and Nepal at a very rapid rate. Although no extensive survey has been completed, rough estimates indicate a population size of around five thousand, and the species is fast disappearing from several areas of its range. The main problems are the damming of rivers for hydroelectric development and irrigation and industrial pollution although direct exploitation (for dolphin oil used as a fishing lure) and accidental capture in fishing nets have also contributed to population declines. The **Indus susu** is found only in Pakistan on the river Indus between Tarbela Dam in the Punjab

and Kotri Barrage in Sind. The total population was estimated to be around five hundred individuals, mainly on a 105-mile (170-km) stretch of river between Guddu and Sukkur Barrages in Sind that makes up the Indus Dolphin Reserve. However, recent surveys suggest that it is more common in Punjab than previously thought whereas estimates for the Sind appear to have been unrealistically high. Within the dolphin reserve, the species has apparently increased, but elsewhere in parts of its former range, populations were exterminated during the late 1970s by illegal hunting and lowering of water levels.

The **Franciscana** or **La Plata river dolphin**, is not so much a river dolphin as a species of estuary and coastal marine habitat. Its status is uncertain although it is known that large numbers have been killed over the last thirty years in shark gillnet fisheries throughout its range in Argentina, Uruguay and Brazil. Although the effects of this mortality on the population at large are still not known, recent declines in accidental catches despite increased fishing effort may indicate that the species itself is in decline.

The **boto** (**boutu** or **Amazon river dolphin**) is the largest of all the river dolphins, inhabiting the largest river system in the world, the vast interconnected Amazon and Orinoco basins that occupy parts of Brazil, Bolivia, Peru, Ecuador, Colombia, Venezuela and Guyana. Although populations are thought to be in a fairly healthy condition, they are recognized as highly vulnerable because of several threats to the Amazon/Orinoco aquatic ecosystems. Those threats include hydroelectric development, deforestation, fishery interactions, and pollution. The greatest threat is posed by dams, which can drastically affect food supplies, movements and hence genetic variability. Very extensive hydroelectric development is planned for Brazil, with little attention given to preserving the riverine environment. Although the level of accidental catch (termed 'by-catch') in fisheries is not thought to be very great at present, river fisheries are expanding very rapidly with increasing use made of monofilament gillnets as well as seine nets and dynamite.

If present trends continue, there may be little time to do anything to save several of the river dolphins; some regional populations are already extinct. Because of growing concerns for this highly vulnerable group, the Cetacean Specialist Group of the IUCN (the World Conservation Union) Species Survival Commission held a workshop at Wuhan in China in October 1986. The results of this were published as 'Biology and Conservation of the River Dolphins', edited by Bill Perrin, Bob Brownell, Jr., Zhou Kaiya and Liu Jiankang (Occas. Paper No. 3 of the IUCN Special Survival Commission (SSC), IUCN, Gland, Switzerland). It has inspired a large amount of research and conservation effort involving specialists from throughout the world, already with some success. We can but hope that these efforts will not be too late.

Ganges susus.

PLATANISTOIDEA — river dolphins

One of the most highly evolved groups of cetaceans forms the superfamily Platanistoidea, otherwise referred to as the 'river' dolphins. Many members live in freshwater, but probably entered rivers from the sea, since some of their fossil ancestors have been found in marine deposits from the Miocene and Pliocene epochs, and the earliest Odontocetes are all marine.

The relationships of living members of the Platanistoidea are still poorly understood. They seem to have evolved quite separately from the Delphinoidea. Those living 'river' dolphins are all small or medium sized animals with long beaks which bear numerous pointed teeth. They also possess pronounced melons and large brains, long beaks with numerous pointed teeth, and flexible necks. They have rather broad short flippers with visible fingers, but poorly developed dorsal fins. Living as they do in turbid water, their vision has become much reduced. In the **Indus** and **Ganges** river dolphins, the lens has been lost altogether.

The Platanistoidea comprise four living families of river dolphin — the Iniidae, the Pontoporiidae, the Lipotidae and the Platanistidae. Each family has representatives occupying different areas of the world.

The family Iniidae includes the **boto** or **Amazon river dolphin** occupying the basin of that name and the neighbouring Orinoco, in Central and South America. Some fossil marine genera (now extinct) from South America are also included within this family. All members of the family have relatively heavily built snouts of intermediate length and large teeth with wrinkled enamel. Their skulls have upturned crests at the margin of the face.

Members of the Pontoporiidae are the only living Odontocetes that have retained a symmetrical skull. Fossils thought to belong to this family have been found in Pliocene marine deposits in South America, suggesting a coastal marine existence as found in the only living representative, the **franciscana**. Some marine fossils from the Late Miocene and Pliocene show features intermediate between the franciscana and the **baiji** or **freshwater Yangtze river dolphin**, indicating a relationship between the Pontoporiidae and the Lipotidae (in which the baiji has recently been placed).

Finally, the family Platanistidae is represented by two Asian freshwater dolphins, the **Ganges** and the **Indus susus**, with distributions centred upon those river systems. They are both small dolphins with a unique pattern of distribution of air sinuses in their skulls, including a large hollow crest on each side of the skull over the eye orbit. Despite possessing some quite primitive characters such as a flexible neck and flippers, their skulls are amongs the most modified of any cetacean.

Dolphins in the North Atlantic

Twenty-two species of dolphins have been recorded from the North Atlantic. Probably the most coastal of species is the **harbour porpoise**, a diminutive rotund animal with a rounded forehead and small triangular fin, and the only phocoenid to occur in the North Atlantic. At the turn of the century, it was widespread in Europe south to the Mediterranean coasts of Spain and Portugal, as well as occurring along the coasts of West Greenland and the eastern seaboard of North America to southern Carolina. However, this century has seen widespread declines and a contraction in range so that now the species is rare in the Mediterranean and Baltic, as well as along the Iberian and French coasts. Since the 1940s, the species has also become rare along the southernmost North Sea coasts of Germany, Holland, Belgium and England. The causes of this decline are not known for certain but over-exploitation of their food, mortality in fishing gear and pollution have all been implicated. On both sides of the Atlantic, concentrations of porpoises tend to occur in the subarctic and cold temperate regions such as west Greenland and the Gulf of St Lawrence, Canada, in Iceland, Scandinavia and northern and western Britain. Since the contractions of their range have been mainly in southern parts, it is possible that oceanographic changes may also have contributed.

The other species of small cetacean that is most likely to be seen in coastal waters is the **bottle-nosed dolphin**, around three times the size of the porpoise with a much larger curved dorsal fin, dark upperparts and pale belly and lower flanks. It has a very wide distribution, from northern Norway and Nova Scotia (Canada) in the north to equatorial West Africa and eastern Central America. Declines have been reported in northern Europe (southernmost North Sea/English Channel, and the Baltic) and in the Mediterranean, over the last half century.

In some localities, concentrations of bottle-nosed dolphins have formed the subject of field studies. Such areas include Sarasota Bay, Florida and Galveston Bay, Texas, in the United States; the Moray Firth in north-east Scotland and Cardigan Bay in west Wales; the coasts of Normandy and Brittany in northern France; and the Sado estuary in Portugal. Most of these populations appear to include at least some core groups that are resident throughout the year.

Harbour porpoises and bottle-nosed dolphins are by no means the only species of small cetacean that may be seen in coastal waters. **White-beaked** and **Risso's dolphins** commonly occur along Atlantic coasts of Scotland and Ireland, the former also being found regularly in the North Sea and cold waters around Iceland, western and northern Norway, off Labrador and Newfoundland in Canada and Cape Cod in north-east United States, whilst the latter species seems to particularly favour warm waters such as occur in the Ligurian Sea within the Mediterranean and around the Atlantic islands of the Cape Verdes, Canaries and Azores. Both are large dolphins, about 10-12 feet in length with tall strongly curved dorsal fins, but white-beaked dolphins have a short beak usually white-tipped, and a distinctive white area on the flanks extending over the back behind the fin whereas the Risso's dolphin has a rounded forehead without a beak, many pencil-like markings over the back and flanks, and the body colouration lightens with age

Further offshore live a wide range of dolphin species. The **Atlantic white-sided dolphin** is common in the cold temperate waters of the northern North Atlantic (off the coasts of Labrador and south-west Greenland, southern Iceland and the Faroes, northern and western Norway and north Scotland). It is closely related to the white-beaked dolphin which it resembles, but it can be distinguished by the long white oval area on the flanks, extending backwards as a yellow ochre band, but with no white over the back behind the fin. Further south its place is taken by the **common dolphin**, a much smaller (six foot) dolphin with long beak, smaller but still distinctly curved dorsal fin, and characteristic hourglass pale colouration to the flanks. This is the commonest dolphin off south-west England, southern Ireland, Brittany and the Bay of Biscay, although it also follows the Gulf Stream northwards off the edge of the continental shelf, coming into coastal waters of west Scotland in midsummer. It is common off the Atlantic coasts of France, Spain and Portugal (where it overlaps with the **striped dolphin**), and around the Azores. In the western North Atlantic, it is commonest between Cape Cod and Cape Hatteras. The similar looking **striped dolphin** is more abundant in warmer waters than the common dolphin and is the commonest species off the coasts of south-eastern United States and in the Mediterranean. It is also a primarily deepwater species but where the two overlap, there is some indication that the common dolphin may be forced into mainly continental shelf waters. The striped dolphin can be distinguished by its shorter beak, and white or light grey V-shaped blaze on the flanks starting from above and behind the eye with one finger narrowing to a point below the fin and a lower one extending towards the tail, and two black lines from the eye, one to the flippers and the other to the anus.

Two dolphin species, the **rough-toothed** and **Fraser's dolphins**, live offshore in the deep waters of the subtropical and tropical Atlantic. They are very little known, but one or other species has been reported from the eastern Caribbean, the Cape Verde Islands and off the coast of Mauritania in North-West Africa. The rough-toothed dolphin has a very distinctive head, rounded with a long tapering beak rather like the neck of a bottle. Fraser's dolphin has a much shorter stubby beak. Sharing those waters but commonly occurring also in coastal regions are the **clymene (short-snouted spinner)** and **long-snouted spinner dolphins** and the **Atlantic spotted dolphin**. The first two have only recently been recognized as separate species, distinguished by the shorter beak and hence fewer teeth in the clymene dolphin. Spotted and spinner dolphins are in fact amongst the commonest of dolphin species within the seas of the tropics. Both are relatively small (about six feet long), slender dolphins. As implied by their name, spotted dolphins have spotting over the backs and flanks although this varies with age (young ones are unspotted) and regional forms. Spinner dolphins have no such distinctive markings but have long slender beaks and, when breaching, they commonly spin on a longitudinal axis.

The **Atlantic hump-backed dolphin** is another tropical species. It is a strange looking dolphin, of similar appearance in many respects to the bottle-nosed dolphin but with a distinct humped back and a keel above and below the tail

Spotted dolphin.

stock. Its distribution is only poorly known but appears to centre on the West African coast between Mauritania and Cameroon.

Of larger species that may be found in the North Atlantic, the **melon-headed whale** and **pygmy killer whale** occupy essentially tropical seas, usually occurring in very deep waters. Because they are rarely close to shore, they are seen only infrequently and little is known about their habits. They are rather similar looking animals, mainly black in colour and overlapping in size, with a slender tapered head (although rather more pointed in the melon-headed whale) and slightly underslung jaw. About twice as large is the related **false killer whale** (so named because it sometimes takes other marine mammals). It is another oceanic species whose range extends northwards into the warm temperate waters of south-eastern United States and South-west Europe (occasionally further north). Rarely seen despite probably being fairly common, the species is best known from the mass strandings that occasionally occur.

One of the commonest of the medium-sized species to occur in subtropical and warm temperate seas is the **short-finned pilot whale**. It is a deepwater species but where such waters come close to the coast, such as in the Canary Islands and the Caribbean, it can be seen nearshore. Because it is so similar to the closely related **long-finned pilot whale** (differing only in being slightly smaller with shorter flippers, and less distinct grey areas on the belly and on the chin), the extent to which they overlap in range is little known. Long-finned pilot whales are common and widely distributed in the cold temperate regions of the North Atlantic, often far offshore, although seasonally they will approach coastal areas such as Newfoundland, Cape Cod, the Faroe Islands and North Scotland. They are also found in the Mediterranean and have been reported further south off the coast of North-West Africa and

Pilot whales.

Cape Hatteras in southern United States although in those areas their range overlaps with short-finned pilot whales.

Few species of small cetaceans endure the cold seas of the high Arctic. Two notable ones are the **beluga** or **white whale** and its relative the **narwhal.** In the North Atlantic, they both occur mainly in Baffin Bay and the Barents Sea, the white whale migrating south to spend the winter in the Davis Strait, Gulf of St Lawrence, and off the coast of north-west Norway. Finally the **killer whale** or **orca** may be seen in polar seas even amongst the pack ice although its distribution extends widely into all latitudes, being seen occasionally in subtropical and tropical seas. Greatest numbers have been recorded around the coasts of Iceland, off central west Greenland, near the Lofoten Islands and off the Møre coast in west Norway. The name 'killer' derives from its habit of feeding upon other marine mammals.

THE BOTTLE-NOSED DOLPHIN

For many people in Europe, there is only one species of dolphin and that is the bottle-nosed dolphin. This is the species most familiar to holidaymakers by the sea; the species most commonly seen in dolphinaria; and the one that on occasions befriends humans and more than any other has led to the general perception of a highly intelligent, friendly and non-aggressive creature worthy of the large number of myths and legends surrounding it.

The bottle-nosed dolphin has a worldwide distribution. It is one of the few species of dolphin that can be truly classed as cosmopolitan, occurring from cold temperate regions to the tropics, in Atlantic, Pacific and Indian Oceans, the Mediterrranean, Red Sea and Black Sea. Although frequently seen in coastal waters including sheltered bays and the mouths of estuaries, equally it may be seen far from shore in deep waters of the main oceans. Off the coasts of North America it ranges from Nova Scotia to Florida, Texas and the Caribbean. In Europe it is sometimes seen as far north as northern Norway, although its main strongholds are north-east Scotland (particularly the Moray Firth), western Ireland, West Wales, north-west France, the Bay of Biscay, Portugal (particularly the Sado estuary) and portions of the Mediterranean. In eastern North America, concentrations occur along the North Carolina coast, off the coast of Texas and in Sarasota Bay, Florida, as well as offshore along the edge of the continental shelf.

In many areas of the world, separate inshore and offshore stocks of bottle-nosed dolphins have been recognized, partly on the basis of their distribution and partly due to differences in their body size and appearance. Inshore forms live often in shallow waters, in sheltered bays, estuaries or lagoons whereas the offshore forms occur in the open ocean or around the margins of oceanic islands and atolls. Where studies have been carried out on populations living close to land, they have revealed a dolphin community divided into discrete groupings of animals often resident in the area with relatively small, overlapping home ranges. Offshore populations, on the other hand, seem to be more prone to seasonal migration, probably reflecting the migratory movements of pelagic fish and squid prey.

Off the coast of the south-eastern United States, the offshore form is not only larger than the coastal form (with a proportionately wider skull and smaller flippers), but also shows consistent differences in its blood constituents (haemoglobin concentrations, packed cell volume, red blood cell count and type of haemoglobin present). This suggests that the two may be genetically isolated from one another, one being best characterized as a cool and deep-water form and the other as a shallow and warm-water form.

Bottle-nosed dolphins eat a wide variety of fish and squid, although in any one area and at any particular season, their diet is probably more restricted, with perhaps four of five species favoured, generally of a size range between 5

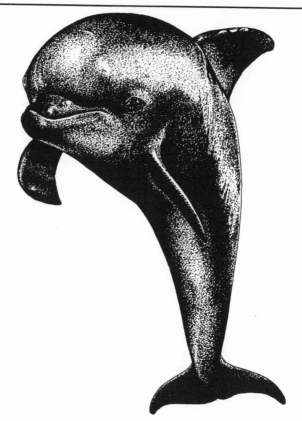

Bottle-nosed dolphin.

and 30 cm (2 and 12 inches) long. These may include fish that range through the water column such as salmon, bass and grey mullet, and also bottom-dwelling fish such as snappers, croakers and seatrouts. Offshore, they capture oceanic squid and shoaling fishes, diving to depths of 500 or 600 metres (1,600 or 2,000 feet) to do so. Where detailed dietary studies have been carried out, it has often been found that the favoured prey species are fish that produce loud sounds. For this reason, it has been speculated that bottle-nosed dolphins may detect and then follow fish prey by listening for the sounds they produce.

From captive studies, it appears that bottle-nosed dolphins require between 4 and 8 per cent of their body weight per day. This would be equivalent to somewhere between three and five stomachfuls of food per day. Mothers and calves probably need to feed more than other categories, and this may determine their behaviour, the areas over which they range, and even who they associate with.

The bottle-nosed dolphin is one of the best studied of all dolphin species. In Florida, south-eastern United States, a community of around a hundred individuals has been studied for nearly a quarter of a century. The average school size within this community is seven dolphins. Although the composition of schools may fluctuate over the course of a day, many associations are relatively stable and long term. The basic unit appears to be the mother-calf bond which can persist over many years. Membership of female bands is also long-lasting, mothers with calves of similar ages tending to form stable associations with one another. These associations are encouraged by the seasonality of reproduction, so that females with similar reproductive cycles tend to associate with one another most closely, resulting in a cohort of calves that may continue to associate closely long after they have become independent of their mothers. Even when males become independent from their mothers and leave the female bands, they congregate in bachelor groups that appear to be based on the relationships established when they were calves. Subadult females may also join these bachelor groups but, on reaching sexual maturity, they tend to return to the female band in which they were born. These genetic ties and long-term associations stretching over many years provide ready conditions for the evolution of co-operative behaviour, a feature that has often been remarked on with respect to this species. This may take the form of co-ordinated feeding, with members of the group collectively herding fish; the aiding of individuals in distress; and 'babysitting'of calves by adult female group members that are not the parent.

With a natural lifespan of 30 to 50 years, bottle-nosed dolphins can afford to have a long period of adolescence, first breeding when they are around 10 to12 years old (possibly slightly later in females than males). In temperate regions at least, most calves are born in spring and summer, after a 12-month gestation period. The calf is suckled for up to 18 months, although it can take fish for itself within 6 months of being born. Generally, an adult female bears a calf every 3-6 years, although if it dies prematurely, she may breed at a shorter interval.

The life of the coastal bottle-nosed dolphin frequently brings it into contact with human activities — fisheries conflicts (both accidental capture in nets and direct takes by fishermen), chemical and biological (sewage) pollution, and sound disturbance from vessels. Although we are often far from clear of the relative importance of these potential threats to local dolphin populations, there are areas (for example Iki Island in western Japan) where large numbers are known to have been killed (in this case, several thousand between 1973 and 1982), whilst several hundred died from algal poisoning along the east coast of the United States between 1987-88, and over the last ten years, carcasses washed ashore have been found with disturbingly high levels of organochlorine chemicals. Until some statutory management of important dolphin habitats is established, we can expect the problem only to get worse.

Dolphin bow-riding large ship.

2

Dolphin Design

Anyone who has stood on the bows of a ship watching a dolphin riding the waves, or had the privilege of swimming amongst dolphins, cannot fail to have been impressed by the ease with which they move through the water. By comparison, we are so poorly adapted to the sea that it is no surprise that our knowledge of its secrets is extremely sketchy. Despite recent advances, we still know less about the lives of dolphins than virtually any other living mammal group.

Generally, dolphins are torpedo-shaped, providing minimum resistance as they travel through water. Many have an upright fin on the back, made of a fibrous fatty material, which may serve for balance, and in some cases help in temperature regulation, although it is clearly not essential any more since a number of species do not have one. All have a large boneless horizontal tail fluke, powered by two muscle masses towards the back which enable it to move up and down, propelling the animal forward. A pair of flippers behind the head is all that remains of ancestral forelimbs. These are used for steering and stability although they appear to be important also in social and sexual contexts as an organ of touch. The hindlimbs have been lost altogether, at least externally — there are still traces of their bony skeleton buried within the abdominal blubber and muscle, the vestigial remains of the pelvic girdle and in some cases the femur.

Like all mammals, dolphins are warm-blooded; they breathe air with lungs which means that they must periodically come to the surface; and they give birth to live young which the mother suckles using milk from her mammary glands.

As warm-blooded mammals, dolphins need to maintain a stable body-core temperature (around 36-7°C). Most land mammals do this by an insulating coat of hair or fur. But dolphins cannot do this because, in water, hair would slow them down, so that the benefits of a streamlined shape would be lost in the extra energy they would need to expend. For this reason, dolphins (and all other cetaceans) have evolved an insulating layer of fat called blubber. Seals, sea-lions, dugongs and manatees all possess blubber as well, living as they do mainly in an aquatic environment.

Fat may also be laid down in other regions of the body — in organs such as the liver, tissues such as muscle, and in bone in the form of oil. The thick layer of blubber is not the only way that dolphins are able to maintain their body temperatures. Within the blubber is a fine network of thin-walled blood capillaries with vascular bundles, which operate a so-called counter-current system whereby heat lost from blood flowing away from the warm body core is partly recovered by closely adjacent inflowing blood. Other ways of conserving heat include a reduction in respiration rate, an increase in metabolic rate, and the reduction of external appendages from which heat would

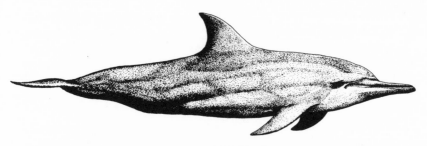

Typical dolphin shape.

otherwise be lost. In cetaceans, all protruding parts are reduced or tucked away. This is one reason why the penis of the male is completely hidden within muscular folds, and the teats of the female are concealed within slits on either side of the genital area.

Although all dolphins have a basically rounded body, larger at the front and tapering towards the back, there are variations in the shape of their heads, some species having long narrow beaks, others short ones, and some no beak at all, possessing instead a blunt snout. In all cetaceans, dolphins and whales alike, the nostrils have moved from their ancestral position in the front of the skull (as found in land mammals) to the top of the skull. This enables them to rise to the surface and take in air without having to propel a large part of the body above water every time. As a consequence, the skull has become telescoped, both the upper and lower jaws extending far forward of the bony entrance to the nostrils. Dolphins have also developed a melon, made of fatty tissue and situated above the upper jaw (termed the rostrum). Its purpose is thought to be to focus sound during echolocation (see Senses on page 34).

Nowadays, dolphins may be found in all the oceans of the world — far into the polar ice, in deep ocean thousands of miles from land, amidst tropical lagoons, in shallow estuaries, even far up freshwater rivers. The evolution of the group has enabled them to exploit virtually every aquatic habitat. They represent supreme adaptation to life in water, and we can but marvel at their specialized existence, perhaps with no little amount of envy that we cannot follow them.

Locomotion

An Olympic swimmer may achieve speeds of 6 miles(9 kilometres) per hour; but a dolphin can attain 40 miles (55 kilometres) per hour. How do they manage to swim so much faster than us?

The secret to the dolphin's ability to travel rapidly and apparently effortlessly through water lies not just in its streamlined shape but also in certain characteristics of its body surface and the way the body can constantly change shape. An examination of the skin of a live dolphin reveals how smooth it is to the touch. The skin cells exude tiny droplets of oil which act as a lubricant and help to reduce friction. These cells may be shed several times a day. Unlike a solid object like a ship, dolphins are able to reduce the turbulence created as they move through the water by having a flexible body in which the blubber is not rigidly fixed to the underlying muscle tissue. As well as the oil secretions, temporary ridges in the skin are thought to help break up and disperse the energy contained in the water particles which pass over the body. When a fluid passes over a streamlined shape, as when a dolphin swims through water, it is continuously displaced in front by the solid body, leaving an equal amount of 'space' immediately behind. Those fluid layers nearest the body cling to it and are thus slowed down the most, thus providing minimum resistance to movement, whilst the more distant layers glide over one another. This is termed 'laminar flow', and is the key to efficient movement through water. Many people have sought to make ships as efficient as dolphins, but are thwarted by those features that have proved impossible to mimic — the structure of its skin and flexibility of the body enabling it so readily to change shape.

Although dolphins only achieve speeds of 40 miles per hour for short bursts, they can travel for sustained periods at 20 to 25 miles(30 to 40 kilometres) per hour when riding the bows of a ship. Bow-riding is perhaps the feature above all others that captures the attention of seafarers. But how, and why, do dolphins engage in this activity, some species more than others?

When a ship moves through the water, it creates a bow wave immediately in front and to the sides of the hull. This wave is formed of water displaced by the vessel, and, since it is being created continuously as the vessel moves forward, it remains stationary in relation to the ship. Bow-riding dolphins may often be seen apparently vying for a particular position. Near the leading edge of the wave is a small region where there is a pressure field exerting sufficient force to propel the animal forward, saving it from expending energy by active swimming. Indeed, if it does not itself remain stationary at the right point, it will not remain in the pressure field. This spot constantly shifts as the vessel pitches on the sea, minutely changing speed and orientation, so that several members of a group of dolphins may get the opportunity to benefit from the bow wave.

Some vessels appear to be much more inclined to attract bow-riding dolphins than others. This is probably due to a number of features — the speed and the size of the vessel, and the underwater noise it produces. Vessels may travel too fast for a dolphin, or equally may be too slow to generate sufficient forward motion to make it worthwhile to bow-ride. Generally, the

White-beaked dolphin breaching.

larger the vessel, the greater the bow wave produced, and some of the most spectacular sights have been of dolphins riding the bow of a huge tanker(see illustration p. 27). Even large whales like the fin whale and blue whale can attract 'bow'-riding dolphins which travel for periods of time close to their heads, as the whale repeatedly breaks the sea surface. On some occasions, when the sea is very rough, dolphins may also bow-ride naturally formed waves.

Although dolphins may be deterred from certain vessels by the sounds of their engines, it seems more likely that they are affected by subtle character-istics of hull shape, combined with vessel speed and by what the dolphin is doing at the time. If it is intent upon seeking or capturing prey, it may be less likely to break off from this important activity to engage in what is probably often sheer pleasure in play.

The buoyancy of water allows a dolphin to move around without needing large limbs to support it. Instead, as we have seen earlier, the external limbs have been reduced to provide dolphins with a streamlined shape for the minimum possible resistance to forward motion. The tail flukes are horizontal flat blades of dense fibrous tissue, attached to the caudal (tail) vertebrae and surrounded by ligaments that extend from the tail-stock. When a dolphin swims, the strong muscles attached particularly to the upper surface of the tail stock move the flukes up and down, this action propelling the animal forward. The upward motion is the power stroke, and during this action, the ligaments are limited in the amount they can extend so that the flukes maintain a flat profile. On the passive downward recovery stroke, the flukes assume an upward curve, spilling water to each side and thus offering least resistance.

The junction between the tail stock and the flukes, and the base of the tail are the main places that are flexible in the dolphin skeleton. The only other site is in the neck but here movement is generally pretty limited. The seven cervical (neck) vertebrae found in nearly all land mammals have become greatly compressed in cetaceans to form only a small part of the vertebral column. In the beluga, narwhal, and some of the river dolphins, all seven neck vertebrae are separate, enabling those animals to move their head around to a relatively large degree. In all other dolphin species, the first two neck vertebrae (called the 'atlas' and the 'axial') are fused together and often some of the vertebrae behind them may in turn be fused to them. This has resulted in very little mobility between the head and the trunk, any movement being almost confined to the vertical plane. Most dolphins can do little more than nod slightly up and down, with scarcely any movement of the head from side to side. But this relative lack of mobility is more than made up for by the ease with which the dolphin can change movement of the entire body, aided by flippers, dorsal fin and tail flukes.

Breathing and diving

When a human diver enters the water without additional air, he or she can only remain submerged for a maximum of two or three minutes before getting into distress, since we usually breathe air fifteen times a minute. Cetaceans, on the other hand, can remain below the surface for extended

Breaching in groups.

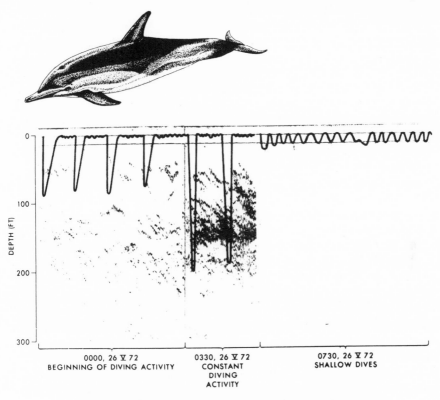

DEPTH (FT)

0

100

200

300

0000, 26 Ⅴ 72
BEGINNING OF DIVING ACTIVITY

0330, 26 Ⅴ 72
CONSTANT
DIVING
ACTIVITY

0730, 26 Ⅴ 72
SHALLOW DIVES

Typical diving cycle of a common dolphin in midsummer

for three periods of the day.

periods. Those species of whale that inhabit the ocean depths, like the sperm whale and beaked whales, may stay submerged for one to two hours. When searching for food, the smaller dolphins usually dive for anywhere between five and fifteen minutes, then surfacing about six times in a single minute (the frequency varies with species, age and activity) before diving again.

When seals are about to dive, they exhale all the air from their lungs. Dolphins, on the other hand, rapidly inhale air when they come to the surface so that when they dive, they take down with them a lungful of air. This pattern of intermittent breathing is referred to as 'apnoea'. Although air in the lungs provides the oxygen necessary for survival, during long dives this becomes exhausted, and cetaceans must then rely upon other sources. The same applies when at great depths (anything below 100 metres) since the water pressure forces any remaining air out of the lungs. Instead, cetaceans store most of their oxygen either in their blood systems or in the muscles.

Even when the alveoli of the lungs have completely collapsed, oxygen may continue to be exchanged because the terminal airways of the lungs are unique in having a rich network of blood capillaries in the lining (referred to as the *retia mirabilia*, meaning 'wonderful nets'). Not only do they have a relatively large total blood volume but also the blood is very rich in haemoglobin, the substance that carries dissolved oxygen around the body. In addition, the muscles themselves possess unusually large amounts of myoglobin, a protein that combines with oxygen from the blood to form a store which can power the muscles that enable cetaceans to move around. Up to half the total oxygen capacity of the animal may be stored in this way.

During dives, cetaceans can also reduce their heart rates (to 10-50 per cent of the rate at the surface) and limit blood flow to the heart and brain. This not only reduces the oxygen debt but also helps to prevent the animal becoming chilled in the relatively cool waters of the deep ocean.

Another feature that places cetaceans apart from most other mammals is their ability to undertake deep dives without suffering the painful condition known as 'the bends', which besets the human diver. Although only some of the larger whales like the sperm whale and bottlenose whales have a reputation for diving down to great depths (which may extend to a staggering 2-3,000 metres), even the smallest dolphins and porpoises can outdive humans. Recent radiotelemetry studies of the diminutive harbour porpoise have shown that it not uncommonly may dive to 120 metres (350 feet) depth.

When a human diver goes below the surface for longer than he or she can hold breath, a cylinder of compressed air is necessary. This is because the air pressure within the lungs must equal or slightly exceed the pressure of the water around them otherwise the lungs will be crushed. Under such compression, the nitrogen in the air dissolves fully into the fluids and tissues of the body. When a diver ascends to the surface, this dissolved nitrogen comes out of solution in the form of bubbles of the gas. They may occur in any part of the body. If those bubbles occur inside a joint, they cause the painful condition known as 'the bends'. If a bubble occurs in the blood (an embolism), it may block a vital artery in the heart or brain and lead to death.

Dolphins, however, are quite unaffected by such pressure effects or the bends, because by contrast they do not breathe air under pressure. As we have seen earlier, when a dolphin dives down, its lungs collapse under the pressure of the water. The walls of the alveoli at the very ends of the lung bronchi where gaseous exchange takes place, become thicker so reducing the rate that gases like nitrogen enter the blood. Thus at a depth of one hundred metres, the lungs have collapsed completely, and the nitrogen invasion rate is reduced to zero. In this manner, a dolphin can safely dive to greater depths without further increase in pressure having an effect. A human diver on the other hand must continue to keep his or her lungs inflated if going deeper, so that the greater the depth the greater the invasion rate of nitrogen and the more nitrogen will dissolve in the body.

When a dolphin returns to the surface after a dive, its lungs gradually expand and the nasal plug that closes the blowhole underwater is forced open. Any used air in the lungs is then emitted in the form of a spout or blow; although often scarcely visible in the smaller dolphins, this cloud of spray always occurs. In the smaller species, the blow may only take a fraction of a second. Despite such a brief period of time at the surface, and a lower breathing rate than terrestrial mammals, including humans, 80 to 90 per cent of the oxygen in the lungs is replaced during one surfacing (contrasted with the 15 per cent in humans).

The nature of the spout is still not entirely clear. Some have thought that the blow is formed by water from around the blowhole being forced into the air, but more recent evidence from electron microscopy has indicated that lining the trachea is a very specialized absorptive layer containing glands which produce secretions that collect at the bottom of the junction between the larynx and the trachea. These secretions are then thought to be removed by the coughing action of exhalation. When a large cetacean surfaces, it leaves behind an oily suspension on the surface, and this could be the result of such droplets, although it may also come from the oily foam that fills the complex system of sinuses found in the head.

A blow often shows up most clearly in polar seas, or, elsewhere, on a cold day. This is due to the condensation of droplets in cold air from the saturated vapour. In the largest cetacean species, which tend to have the biggest blows and often spend longest at the surface, the spout is generally very clear and indeed often may be used in species identification. But for most of the species we are concerned with in this book, the blow is small and scarcely visible.

The senses

Six senses dominate the lives of animals: sight, sound, taste, touch, smell and the magnetic sense. Animals vary in the degree to which one or other of these senses is important. Although using all these senses to an extent, we humans have made particular use of sight, sound and touch. We have evolved flexible joints and an opposable thumb enabling us to manipulate objects and perform tasks. A voice box has contributed greatly to our ability to speak, and this has played an important role in the development of language, and hence of culture. And, finally, vision has played a central role in our day-to-day activities.

Cetaceans, including dolphins, living as they do in an aquatic medium, have developed those senses that serve best in that environment, given the constraints that adaptation of form and physiology have imposed upon them. The streamlining of their bodies with consequent reduction of external limbs has limited the extent to which they can perform manual tasks. The filtering of light by water has resulted in vision becoming often secondary, particularly for those species living in muddy rivers or at great depths. On the other hand, sound is transmitted through water almost five times faster than through air, due to the greater density of water. This has led to whales and dolphins developing sound production and hearing as their major sense. But first let us examine the role of some of the other senses.

Taste and smell both involve the reception of chemical stimuli. In toothed whales, including all dolphins, studies of their anatomy have indicated an absence of olfactory bulbs or nerves, the normal receptors for smell. It therefore seems that dolphins have no sense of smell, at least in the form that exists in most mammals. Many terrestrial mammals use chemical substances (termed 'pheromones') to mark territories, and convey messages about sex. Although pheromone production and detection has not been demonstrated for cetaceans, it is possible that in certain situations, and at close quarters, these might operate. As yet, however, it is difficult to see what might serve as receptors for such stimuli.

Dolphins do have apparent taste receptors at the base of the tongue, and the region of the brain associated with taste is well developed. Experimental studies in captivity have shown that **common dolphins, bottle-nosed dolphins** and **harbour porpoises** all have the ability to discriminate between different chemicals, even small differences in the concentration of citric acid. However, taste in dolphins appears to differ in various respects from that observed in other mammals. Whereas dolphins detect chemicals which for us produce sensations of sour, bitter, salty and sweet, they do not necessarily elicit the same responses. For example, chemicals that we find bitter and distasteful do not seem to trouble the dolphin at all.

Although external protrusions such as limbs have been sacrificed for greater streamlining, those that do exist appear to serve as important tactile organs. Dolphins may frequently be observed rubbing their skin against one another, or touching with flippers or dorsal fin. We normally view the penis solely as a sexual organ, but in cetaceans it has an additional tactile function, being used to explore the immediate physical and social environment. Dolphins commonly erect their penises, and not necessarily in a sexual context, although humans tend to jump to those conclusions as happened for example in the recent court case of a man accused of sexually molesting the 'friendly' dolphin Freddie at Amble, Northumberland. In fact it is often very difficult to distinguish whether or not there is a sexual component in the use of a penis by dolphins. Studies of captive animals have shown that penis display including actual entry of another commonly occurs between individuals during social interactions. It can take place at any time of the year between and within all age groups, and between members of the same sex as much as of the opposite sex. Such courtshiplike behaviour may function as a greeting when individuals meet after a period of absence. It also appears to serve as a means for establishing dominance, since it is most often exhibited by the dominant member of the group, the subordinate assuming a passive 'female' posture, swimming upside down with belly up. Other greeting displays involve rubbing their flanks or bellies against one another, and touching with the beak or the flipper.

Clearly the skin in some parts of the body is highly sensitive to touch. Additionally, tiny hairs persist around the beak some time after birth, and adult river dolphins possess whiskers on their long and sensitive snouts. These serve not only to indicate rapidly when the sea surface is reached so that the blowhole can open at exactly the right moment, but, in the case of the river dolphin, allow ready detection of pressure changes amongst the turbulent muddy waters of their habitat.

It is only in the top 60 metres (200 feet) that sufficient light enters the water column for vision to be of much use. Water is much less transparent to light than air, and suspended particles such as plankton and silt absorb and scatter light, which is very quickly absorbed or reflected. Indeed, at 10 metres (30 feet) depth, 90 per cent of the light has been lost, and this rises to 99 per cent at 40 metres (130 feet) depth. Although it is pitch black at the depths that many whales live, luminescent squid upon which they commonly feed may produce sufficient light to be detected visually.

Those dolphins possessing a beak and eyes set forward on the head have binocular vision which enables them to see forwards and downwards. Others with larger more rounded heads are not able to see immediately in front of their jaws, and for the most part have monocular vision.

Tests on captive **bottle-nosed dolphins** have shown that they have good visual acuity. They are able not only to discriminate the fine details of objects in water but are pretty good also in air, as anyone watching a dolphin leaping through a hoop in a dolphinarium can testify. Although at a distance of a metre, aerial vision was poor compared with underwater vision, at 2.5 metres there was little difference between the two. It is thought that the reason dolphins can see equally well in both air and water is the great elasticity of their eye lenses, which are relatively highly movable, and can result in the pupil constricting under bright light either to form two apertures or a U-shaped slit, and in dim light using the whole range of the eye with pupil dilation. The precise means by which visual acuity is achieved is still a matter of debate. Some suggest that they can directly modify the shape of the lens despite lacking the ciliary muscles surrounding the lens that other mammals use to achieve this; others suggest that instead they use the peripheral area of the retina to form images, the processing of which is helped by large optic nerve fibres connected to giant ganglion cells.

Although both rod- and cone-like receptor cells (the same that humans have for distinguishing colour and contrast) are present in dolphin eyes, trials with captive dolphins have been unsuccessful in teaching them to discriminate among blue, green or red mono-chromatic light. This inability to distinguish colours was supported by other studies using monochromatic light of different wavelengths.

In the course of adapting to life underwater, dolphins have lost external protrusions such as ear pinnae, which would provide resistance to body movement. But they do have excellent hearing, and from a small hole in the side of the head leads a passage to the cochlea, the spiral cavity of the inner ear. Unlike in terrestrial mammals, the cochlea is isolated from the skull by foam-filled air spaces. This enables the dolphin to determine the direction of any sound that it has detected because athe sound will generally be amplified by passing through the air spaces, thus making it appear louder on the side from which it comes.

The path taken by sound to the inner ear still remains a subject of much debate. The British zoologists Francis Fraser and Peter Purves concluded that dolphins receive sound from outside the head via the water-filled channel referred to as the external auditory meatus, whilst the American zoologist Ken Norris suggested that sound is received via tissue conduction through the fat layer of the lower jaw, aided by the isolation of the ear bullae by means of a bubbly foam in the way described above.

Sound is used in two ways — for communication and for echolocation. Dolphins, porpoises and toothed whales communicate by producing a wide variety of high frequency sounds — whistles, pulsed squeals, screams or barks, generally in the frequency range 1-20 kHz. These sounds are thought to be produced either in the nasal plug region or in the larynx, or perhaps in both. In the case of the former theory, compressed air passes as a series of pulsed sounds from the nasal sacs behind the plugs to the dorsal sacs where they are stored before recycling to the lower sacs for the next burst of sounds. Focusing of sound is achieved by altering the shape of the melon (the fatty tissue contained within the forehead) and thus changing its focal length. In the case of the latter theory, focusing of sound is thought to be achieved by its reverberation off various parts of the skull.

In addition to sounds produced for communication, dolphins also obtain information about their immediate environment, including potential prey,

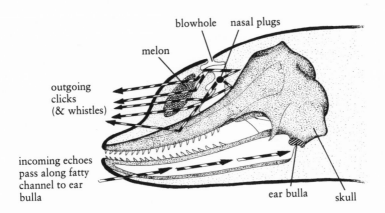

blowhole   nasal plugs

melon

outgoing
clicks
(& whistles)

incoming echoes
pass along fatty
channel to ear
bulla

ear bulla   skull

The apparent routes travelled by sound to and from an echolocating dolphin.

by echolocation — the production of intense short broadband pulses of sound in the ultrasonic range (from about 0.25 to 220 kHz). These clicks are typically less than one millisecond in duration and may be repeated many times per second, although the echo of a pulse is received first before another is emitted.

Like whistles, clicks are thought to be produced in the region of the nasal plugs and emitted forwards in a narrow beam through the melon. They function by bouncing off objects in their path, so producing echoes from which the animal is able to build up an acoustic picture of its surroundings, making use of their form and sound intensity to help identify size, shape and orientation of the object. The time lapse between making the sound and receiving its echo indicates the distance that the object is from the dolphin. This remarkable sensory system has evolved independently in a variety of animal groups, ranging from bats and dolphins to oilbirds and cave swiftlets, all animals that have to hunt fast-moving prey in darkness.

Experiments on captive **bottle-nosed dolphins** have shown that at a metre range they can discriminate targets separated by less than one centimetre. How this is achieved is still not clear. It has been suggested that the arrangement of bones in the skull may serve as a parabolic reflector focusing sounds in the melon after production in the nasal plug area. Alternatively, sound focusing may take place at the interface between the melon and seawater. The shape of the beam for different pulses can vary greatly, whilst dolphins have been shown to emit two pulses simultaneously, directed at different angles to left and right of the head. As noted above, when the sound echo

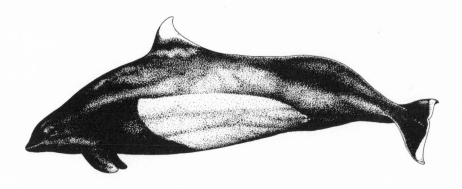

Dall's porpoise.

returns, it is thought to be received through the oil-filled sinuses in the lower jaw, where it is channelled to the inner ear.

The final sense to be considered is perhaps the least known, that of biomagnetism. Many animals, from birds to bacteria, are known to be capable of detecting the earth's magnetic field. This has been demonstrated most convincingly in birds under certain situations, though there is evidence that even humans have this ability. Studies of the anatomy of several cetacean species (including **bottle-nosed dolphin, common dolphin** and **Dall's porpoise**) have revealed tiny quantities of a magnetic material (termed 'magnetite') in the soft tissue covering the brain, evidence that they have the capability to sense the earth's magnetic field and possibly use it for navigation. In Britain, an examination by Margaret Klinowska of the sites of live strandings of mainly open-ocean whales and dolphins indicated a link with local magnetic field lines, most occurring where magnetic contours ran perpendicular rather than parallel to the coast. One interpretation of this is that cetaceans navigate by following magnetic contours when they cannot use other cues such as physical features. In some localities this can bring them directly towards the coast where they may get into difficulties and strand. On the other hand, attempts at similar correlations in other parts of the world have been less successful, whilst the only experimental study with cetaceans, involving two bottle-nosed dolphins, failed to show any response to changes in a magnetic field or its intensity.

Killer whale about to capture sea-lion.

3

Feeding

Diet

Members of the order Odontoceti typically have a long row of even, conical teeth, suitable for grasping rapidly moving prey, usually either fish or squid. Those with long narrow jaws and numerous small sharp teeth (anywhere between 80 and 220) have powerful muscles at the rear of the lower jaw which are thought to help in grasping relatively small fish. Examples are **common dolphin, white-beaked, white-sided** and **dusky dolphins**. **Pilot whales** and **Risso's dolphin**, on the other hand, have broader jaws and fewer teeth (between 14 and 48), concentrated towards the front of each jaw, and muscles most developed around the cheek bones and the rear part of the upper jaw. Those species feed primarily upon squid, prey that are generally broader and probably less manageable than fish. The **bottle-nosed dolphin** possesses between 72 and 104 teeth, and has jaws intermediate in size and shape between the small beaked oceanic dolphins and the larger **Risso's dolphin**. This is thought to reflect a relatively catholic diet that includes a very wide variety of fish ranging from those living on or near the sea bottom to free-swimming shoaling fish, as well as squid.

Killer whales have broad jaws with only a small number (40-48) of large, conical teeth, and very powerful muscles to the rear of the upper jaw. This makes the jaw capable of holding large prey that are likely to resist capture. The species has one of the most catholic diets of all cetaceans, ranging from a variety of fish and squid to birds and other marine mammals.

The **beluga** or **white whale** and the **narwhal** have even fewer teeth, the former having between 32 and 44 teeth, whilst the latter has merely a pair of teeth in the upper jaw, one of which is extruded in the male (and occasionally in the female) to form a spiralled tusk. In those cases, the teeth may no longer be the primary means of capturing prey, and, instead, they are believed to use suction and to emit a jet of water to dislodge prey such as bottom-living fish and molluscs. Both have highly flexible necks which allow them to scan a relatively broad area of the sea bottom and pursue the more mobile prey. Belugas also have the ability to change the shape of their lips which might aid any method of feeding involving suction. The diet of both species is varied, including squid, fish and crustaceans, and in the case of the beluga, worms and molluscs.

Porpoises (members of the family Phocoenidae) typically have between 52 and 112 characteristically spade-shaped teeth which are set at an acute angle in the jaw to help the shearing action of feeding. They also may employ suction during feeding on the bottom. Their diet is varied, though they mainly eat either open-water or bottom-living fish. Most porpoises have fused neck vertebrae which makes it difficult for them to move their heads around, but in the case of the **finless porpoise** which feeds around sand-

Bottle-nosed dolphin capturing fish.

banks and river or estuary bottoms upon fish (such as sandeels), squid and crustaceans (particularly prawns), some of these are unfused for greater mobility. Unlike other members of the family, the **Dall's porpoise** has tiny spade-shaped teeth, numbering 76-116, which are scarcely functional, but instead the species possesses a ribbed palate which enables it to grasp slippery squid. A similar evolutionary course has been taken by some other squid feeders like the beaked whales.

The final group to consider is the river dolphins, whose specialized existence has demanded distinctive adaptations. Living as they do mainly in the turbid muddy waters of tropical rivers, they have virtually dispensed with vision, relying instead upon echolocation for finding prey. They possess numerous (96-240) conical teeth which near the back of the jaw are thickened at the base, but at the front appear long and pointed. Several of the neck vertebrae are unfused giving rise to a flexible neck which, along with the long slender beak, allows them to twist and turn to capture their prey of mainly solitary, bottom-dwelling fish and prawns. Some species will also take other prey, including squid and octopus, crabs, molluscs, small turtles and even possibly waterbirds. During capture of large food items, a river dolphin may tear the fish into pieces before swallowing. If it is hard-bodied, it will be forced to the back of the mouth where the broader-based teeth are used for crushing and chewing of the prey.

Feeding behaviour

Unlike the great baleen whales, which make use of their large mouths to either gulp or skim aggregations of prey from the water, dolphins tend to rely more upon chasing relatively fast-moving prey. But first they must find that food, and in the great expanses of ocean inhabited by many of the species, this is no small task. Fish and squid, which make up the great majority of the prey of various dolphin species, are not distributed evenly through the oceans. Like their own prey, which may be tiny planktonic plants and animals, fish and squid concentrate in areas of high nutrient production. These may be where water masses of different temperature meet, or where the sea bottom shelves away to form canyons or valleys, or where tides transport nutrients from other areas or the sea bottom.

In all those situations, nitrates and phosphates, which are the source of nutrition for planktonic plants, are brought up in the water column to the surface layers where the plants can make use of sunlight for photosynthesis. Some parts of the world are more productive than others, for example cold temperate and polar regions and along the boundaries of certain cool currents in otherwise warm water areas. Those regions often show strong seasonality, and during springtime when sunlight hours are lengthening, sea temperatures rise, and seas calm down allowing stratification of the water (which can trap nutrients in a middle layer called the thermocline); they provide ideal conditions for planktonic growth and reproduction. These areas form the focal point for a wide variety of marine predators — fish, squid, seabirds and sea mammals, many feeding upon each other in a complex food web.

Within a broad area of relatively high productivity, there will be particular localities that are especially rich. These will not necessarily be situated in precisely the same spot from day to day or even hour to hour, since various factors such as winds, diurnal and tidal rhythms may all affect their distribution, and so dolphins must constantly be on the move, searching out their food.

Most dolphins travel in groups which are broader than they are long. In this way they can scan a large area both visually and acoustically, using broad-band echolocation clicks, and yet still keep in contact with one another by breaches (leaps out of the water), tail slaps, whistles and squeals. There is often a high degree of co-operation. In some cases, the mere presence of an individual vigorously feeding may attract others, but often group members appear to operate as a co-operative unit, as when some individuals herd shoals of fish towards others in the group. Corralling of prey in this manner has been seen in several species, including **common, spinner and spotted dolphins, bottle-nosed, dusky and white-beaked dolphins.**

Another method of trapping prey is to force it to the surface which functions rather like a wall. When fish shoals are driven upwards in this manner, some of them fly through the air to escape capture. However, in so doing

Dolphin chasing and splitting fish shoal.

they make themselves susceptible to capture by predatory seabirds, which are forever keeping an eager eye for surface feeding dolphins so that they may take advantage of prey brought into reach from deeper waters. This is probably a major reason why a number of seabird species have been seen associating with cetaceans.

Some dolphins even pursue their prey onto land. For example, **humpbacked dolphins** in the tropics have been observed sliding onto sandbanks in pursuit of fish. **Killer whales** have taken this a stage further, and in some regions of the world (for example along the coast of Patagonia), they purposefully strand to capture seals and sea-lions whilst they are ashore (see illustration on p. 41). A large male may grab a seal on a rising tide, drag it back into the sea, and toss it repeatedly into the air before the unfortunate animal is dismembered. On such occasions the individual that captured the seal may subsequently stay back to allow one or more companions to feed upon it. This level of co-operation is really quite advanced and suggests that individuals come from stable family groups. Indeed, some evidence to this effect has been obtained from genetic analysis and close study of recognizable individuals.

Recently, in northern Norway, killer whales have been filmed underwater using another specialized technique for food capture, referred to as 'carousel feeding'. A group of killer whales swims actively under and around a shoal of herring. As they do so, they often show the white undersides towards the fish and may emit large bubbles close to the ball of herring. The whales then make a loud banging sound by tail-slapping in the midst of the shoal and this appears to stun the fish which are then picked out and eaten. In 75 per cent of cases, tail-slaps led to the stunning of one or more fish. Such feeding sessions can last anywhere between 10 minutes and 3 hours.

Carousel feeding has also been observed with dusky dolphins when feeding on anchovies in Patagonia. Here, the dolphins swim around a dense shoal of fish and drive it to the surface. Any fish that break away from the ball are chased back again. While dolphins swim around and under the shoal, one dolphin at a time will break rank and rapidly move through the centre or periphery of the ball of fish, coming out the other side with up to five anchovies in its mouth. If the dolphin group is small, feeding lasts only around five minutes, for they appear not to be able to hold the shoal at the surface for long. However, if neighbouring dolphin groups join up with them, the fish ball often becomes larger, and the feeding session can last several hours. This may be one reason why small groups of dolphins join up together to feed.

The co-ordination of feeding activities implies some means of communication between group members. During feeding bouts, dolphins not only emit trains of ultrasonic clicks, sometimes so rapid that they make a buzzing sound, but also may make a variety of whistles. The clicks serve primarily to locate prey but may have an additional function of stunning the fish with the pressure waves created by blasts of sound. In experimental studies, fish subjected to high energy sound in a tank become disoriented and even immobilized, which suggests that at least under certain circumstances, echolocation may actually stun fish, though generally at higher sound intensities than dolphins are usually capable of.

As we have seen above, loud sounds can also be made by the physical actions of dolphins. This may take the form of tail-slapping, but also can involve aerial leaps. During the herding of fish shoals, dolphins tend to breach head first re-entering the water the same way. In the middle of a feeding bout, leaps end mainly with animals slapping the surface of the water with their sides, belly or back. These leaps create loud, sharp sounds underwater and occur mainly around the periphery of the fish shoal. As with other aspects of carousel feeding, this action may serve to frighten fish into a tight ball for easier prey capture. Towards the end of a feeding session and afterwards, aerial activity becomes more varied and may include somersaults and spins. At this stage, dolphins appear to be engaging in mainly social activity, and it may signify the end of feeding to neighbouring groups.

Not all dolphins forage in large groups. Some, such as the **river dolphins**, **hump-backed dolphins** and most **porpoises**, generally hunt singly or in small groups, even where large numbers occur over a wide area. All these species tend to feed on bottom-living prey, and it could be that since those prey are usually far from the sea surface, the co-operative surface herding activities displayed by the more open-ocean dolphin species cannot so easily operate. Another consideration may be the more solitary nature of bottom-living fish and squid, but this cannot be the entire reason, since in several cases (for example, **harbour porpoises** upon species such as whiting and sandeels), they also feed on fish that form large shoals.

Energy budgets

Food provides animals with the necessary energy for life. At certain stages in its life, an animal may require more energy than at others, for example during infancy for rapid growth; during pregnancy and lactation to nourish the young; and prior to times of food shortage or unfavourable weather, when energy losses outweigh gains.

The balance between energy inputs and outputs is termed the energy budget, and it governs entirely the annual cycle of activities exhibited by dolphins.

As we have seen earlier, during certain times of the year food may be much more abundant than at others. At those times, dolphins should be able to assimilate more energy and excesses over individual requirements may be used for growth and/or reproduction.

Some prey types have higher energy contents than others. For example, the calorific values (a measure of energy content) of fish that live in the middle water may vary between 4 and 12 kJoules per gram body weight, whereas squid have rather lower values at about 3-3.5 kJoules per gram body weight. Amongst North Atlantic fish, the values are particularly high

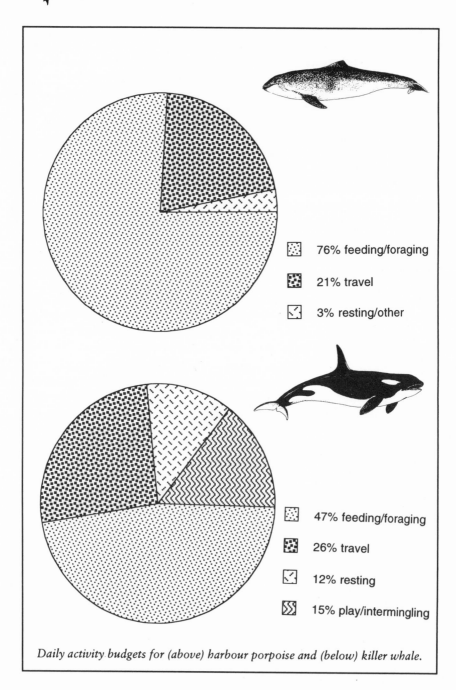

76% feeding/foraging

21% travel

3% resting/other

47% feeding/foraging

26% travel

12% resting

15% play/intermingling

Daily activity budgets for (above) harbour porpoise and (below) killer whale.

in members of the family Clupeidae (which includes sprat and herring), and Scombridae (such as mackerel), with values around 7-12 kJoules per gram weight. Fish of the Gadidae family (cod, whiting, and saithe) tend to have lower calorific values, between 4 and 7 kJoules per gram weight. In those instances, all other things being equal, one might expect a dolphin to select those prey with the highest energy content to satisfy its needs with the minimum of effort. But matters are generally more complicated than this, because all other things are rarely equal. Some fish will be more abundant than others, some will be easier to catch, certain species will be more digestible, or contain particularly high quantities of fat, or protein or some essential vitamin, and there may be seasonal differences in food preferences. All these factors may play a role in the food choice of a dolphin.

Around the Shetland Islands during summer, the **harbour porpoise** is known to feed upon sandeel, herring and various gadoid fish such as whiting, Norway pout and saithe. In winter, sandeels bury into the sand, and herring move away from the region, and it seems likely that porpoises have to change their diets to include greater quantities of flatfish such as flounder, sole and dab, as well as some bottom-living members of the Gadidae. Flatfish have lower energy contents than pelagic fish such as clupeids, and with such prey tending to occur at low densities and to be more dispersed, porpoises are likely to have a less favourable energy balance during this period. We might therefore expect most growth to occur during the summer months, with some provision for energy storage in the blubber to see the animal through any difficult times during winter.

Studies of the energy budget of the harbour porpoise suggest that during 74 days of summer feeding, a 50 kg adult consumes about 70 grams of food per kilogram body weight per day (i.e. about 3.5 kg of fish in a day). For the remaining 291 days, the daily feeding rate declines to an average of maybe 35 grams per kilogram body weight (i.e. about 1.8 kg of fish in a day).

During pregnancy, particularly the latter half when the foetus is growing fastest, a female porpoise or dolphin is likely to have increased energy demands. This will be further accentuated once the calf is born and the mother has to provide it with fat-rich milk to promote rapid growth in an otherwise hostile environment where its small surface area-volume ratio in comparatively cool waters puts it at risk of hypothermia. It is therefore perhaps not surprising that most porpoise calves are born around midsummer and are reared in an environment of maximum food abundance.

Narwhals sparring.

• 4 •

Behaviour

One of the most obvious features of dolphins to a casual observer is their sociability. Even if members of a particular species may spend portions of their lives alone, group-living almost invariably occurs at one time or another, and, for several species, is the norm. Why do dolphins, or indeed any animal, live in groups? One potential disadvantage must be that individuals then have to compete with one another for food resources and access to mates. There are four possible advantages. The first was explored in the last chapter: that groups can help one another both find and then capture food. A second advantage is that groups provide better defence against predators: the well known maxim of safety in numbers works not only by a group being able to offer greater resistance to a predator but also the individual probability of being attacked is reduced. The third advantage is that group-living enables individuals to meet one another for mating. Since they often live in great expanses of ocean, if they were mainly solitary, the chances of meeting for reproduction would be much reduced. Finally, living in groups can help spread the costs of calf rearing. 'Babysitting', where an adult other than the parent may stay by a calf, has been observed in several species. This behaviour enables the mother to dive to depths that are out of range of the calf in order to find food for herself without leaving the calf on its own unprotected from predators. In some species, 'aunties' may even help by suckling the young.

Given the above considerations, it is not surprising that for many dolphin species, group size increases at certain times of the year, in association with particular activities — mating and calving, feeding on large concentrations of food, and making long-distance movements.

The social organization of dolphin groups is still not clearly understood, but where it has been studied, the group seems to have as its basis the mother-calf bond. The extent to which individuals remain within a group can vary greatly between species. **Killer whales**, for example, appear to show very srong social cohesion. Studies by Ken Balcomb, Mike Bigg and others on the West Coast of North America over the last twenty years have indicated that members of the group remain together for life, and groups (or 'pods', as they are termed) may persist from generation to generation. This has led to members of different pods having distinct song dialects, rather as do semi-isolated populations of many songbirds. The size of these pods typically varies from four to forty individuals, although temporary coalitions of several pods may occur, to give groups up to a hundred individuals. On those occasions, generally all pods in a region participate. There is much body contact and males often erect their penises as if in display, frequently in the vicinity of other males. The function of this particular behaviour is not really known but it may serve as a means for sizing up one another in competition for

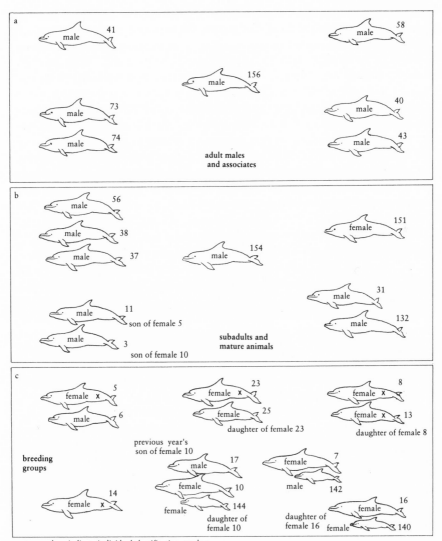

note: numbers indicate individual classification number
x=genetic marker indicates these are related
typical associations indicated by pairings
approximate ages indicated by relative sizes

Bottle-nosed dolphin group structure.

mates, or, alternatively, could simply be a greeting symbolizing non-aggression.

Pilot whales are also thought to show this phenomenon of temporary group coalition, although the identity of individual pods is usually not known so there is no firm evidence that large aggregations involve separate pods. However, year-round observations in the eastern North Atlantic reveal such

Group formation under water.

big groups only at certain times of year, during that period when peak mating occurs. Furthermore, genetic analysis of entire pods captured in the Faroe Islands indicate that adult males are not necessarily responsible for mating within the group, suggesting that different pods must merge at some time or other for out-breeding (mating between members of separate groups) to take place. In **killer whales**, males bond strongly with their mothers, with associations lasting for extended periods; genetic evidence suggests the same may be true for pilot whales.

Whilst **killer whale** pods have been found, at least in some localities, to have a very stable group membership, the smaller delphinids that have been studied (for example, **bottle-nosed, dusky** and **spinner dolphins**) appear to have a much more fluid social structure. Individuals may move from group to group within weeks, days or even hours. However, although they may be away from a group for periods of several weeks or more, the absence is not necessarily permanent. **Bottle-nosed dolphins** in Florida, for example, show short-term individual movements between communities, but only rarely permanent immigration and emigration.

Loose affiliations with individuals associating with one another for variable lengths of time are commonplace, particularly between members of the same sex. **Bottle-nosed dolphins** in Florida may form groups segregated in a variety of ways. As noted earlier, females with their calves are the most permanent associations, with such pairings often joining together to form larger groups, which may be composed of related females. Groups of only subadult males, adult females, or, less commonly, subadult females may also occur.

Breeding groups rarely contain adult males, which seem to be more inclined to move from group to group, mainly for mating purposes. The bond between males is very strong and has been known to last over a period of at least fifteen years.

The precise mating system of any dolphin species remains uncertain because there is insufficient information on paternity and genetic relatedness. There is not much evidence of long-lasting monogamous male-female pairs of dolphins. For monogamy to be favoured by natural selection, there would have to be a benefit in terms of a higher chance of survival of the young. This generally means that males could help care for the young by providing them with food and protecting them from predators. In cetaceans, however, all the early nourishment for calves has to come from the mother through suckling, and males play no part in parental care (except in some cases where they may defend young against predators). In fact, for several animal groups, including mammals, monogamy appears to be quite unusual, and instead, either polygyny or promiscuity seem to be most common.

If there is a resource which is predictable and therefore defendable, then a polygynous mating system may arise where a male can defend an area from other males, with sufficient food available to maintain both the male and a group of females (plus young) over an extended period. In this way the male will have the opportunity to mate with several females. However, most dolphin species do not confine themselves to small areas, but have to range around to find prey, and in most cases there is little opportunity for any form of territorial defence. It is therefore difficult for males to monopolize groups of females, and so we should expect them to have promiscuous mating systems rather than monogamous or polygynous ones. Most of the genetic evidence available to date in fact supports this notion.

Communication

We have seen in an earlier chapter that group living has several advantages. However, because it seems that during the course of their lives dolphins have to cover large areas in their quest for food, they are presented with the potential difficulty of keeping in touch with one another. They have developed various means of communication to overcome this. Some of these are visual cues — breaching above the surface of the water, flipper- and tail-slapping, and 'spy-hopping' (where the head is held above the water). All these draw attention to an individual's presence and may provide others with information about its position and activity, perhaps even its age, sex and reproductive condition.

However, the primary means of communication for dolphins is sound. Their vocal repertoire is very varied and may include squeaks and whistles,

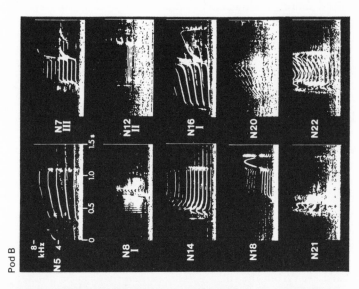

Killer whale song dialects

squawks and groans, rattles, clicks and buzzes to name but a few of the epithets humans have used to describe the sounds. They can be divided into pulsed sounds such as clicks and burst pulses (chirps, chuckles and click-trains), and unpulsed sounds like squeaks and whistles. Not all families produce both kinds of sound.

Members of the family Delphinidae (including the **dolphins, killer whales** and **pilot whales**) produce whistle-like calls and pulsed squeals usually in the frequency range 1-20 kHz, as well as clicks up to about 220 kHz, for echolocation. **Porpoises** (family Phocoenidae) and **river dolphins** (family Platanistidae), on the other hand, appear to produce only clicks and bursts of clicks mainly between 1 and 150 kHz, presumably used primarily for echolocation. It is unclear how they might communicate with one another acoustically except by these high frequency clicks which tend to be produced almost constantly. In the family Monodontidae, **narwhals** produce narrow band pulses (with the range 500 Hz-24 kHz), and longer tonal whistles (mainly between 300 Hz and 10 kHz), whilst white whales produce whistle-like signals (250 Hz-20 kHz) as well as short broadband clicks (40-120 kHz). White whales are thought to be one of the most vocal and varied of all songsters with an amazing range of squeaks, trills, whistles and belches that can be heard even from the surface. This caused them to be dubbed 'sea canaries' by mariners of past centuries.

One important function of the sounds made by dolphins appears to be that of identification — the location of the animal, its sex, status, emotional or activity state, and perhaps even its individual identity. Detailed studies of the contexts in which different calls are made have taken place for a number of dolphin species. They show, for example, that when whistles and squeaks are used, they seem to relate to increased excitement — arousal of the animal during feeding or some threatening confrontation with another individual. In both the **long-finned pilot whale** and **bottle-nosed dolphin**, the repetition rate of whistles increased from a lolling state (low arousal), through transiting (movement from one area to another), reaching a peak during feeding or threatening behaviour (high arousal). On the other hand, in **pilot whales**, whistles showed little variation in frequency (i.e. pitch) when animals were lolling or transiting, the modulation of the whistle increasing with increased excitement or fear.

Tonal pulses may also vary depending upon the context in which they are made. In the **bottle-nosed dolphin** (and at least some other small social delphinids), clicks are made primarily during navigation and hunting; squawks are associated with play, chases or aggressive encounters; yelps occur during courtship and mating; buzzing click-trains when individuals threaten one another; and squeaks, cracks and pops when animals are alarmed, frightened or distressed in some way. During periods of rest and when a predator such as a killer whale is approaching (but before it is actually threatening a dolphin), animals are usually silent.

High frequency clicks travel only short distances and so are unlikely to be used for communication except with small groups in close contact with one another. Unpulsed whistles, however, carry better over long distances (perhaps to a few kilometres) and so may be useful for species living at least some of the time in larger groups, such as **bottle-nosed** and **spinner dolphins**, whereas the relatively non-social species like **porpoises** may have less need for longer distance communication used in group organization/cohesion.

Some whistles are thought to serve as a signature, to communicate the position of an individual, and perhaps to aid group cohesion during normal travel and foraging. For this to function, the individual making the whistle must be recognizable. This has been demonstrated both for captive and wild dolphins, although recognition has not necessarily been of its individual identity but may be of group identity. A male spotted dolphin, for example, was captured from a school (i.e. group of dolphins) and started to whistle almost continuously, presumably in distress. Those calls were recorded and played back to other wild dolphins. Members from the same school fled in response to the playbacks whereas those from another group approached with curiosity.

The extent to which signature whistles provide individual identity may vary between the sexes and between age groups. A recent study of **bottle-nosed dolphins** in Western Australia revealed that whereas females and calves produced one whistle type (the 'signature' whistle), most or all of the time, that could be recognized individually even between related dolphins, males produced a greater variety of whistles and their whistle repertoires changed more over time than females. Three males formed an alliance which brought them together for an extended period (three years) during which they started to co-operatively herd females into the group. At the same time, the males converged on one whistle type which then became the most frequent one used in the repertoires of all three animals. This mimicry and social learning is the basis for the development of dialects and is commonly observed also in songbirds. Amongst mammals it is rare, occurring otherwise mainly in primates including humans.

Killer whales, studied in the coastal waters of British Columbia, have also been shown to have distinct vocal dialects which, like humans, can occur between neighbouring groups, interacting and thus affecting one another by imitation. Killer whales live in extended matriarchal family groups which are very stable. Although they can produce a variety of sounds including clicks and whistles, most of the sounds heard when the animals are spread out and foraging are repetitious and stereotyped pulsed calls which may be organized into discrete categories. Twelve distinct calls of this type have been recognized as coming from these groups that are more or less resident in the area and these may all be heard over a very short period whatever behaviour they are engaged upon. Other smaller transient groups occur in the area, and by contrast are generally silent, presumably reflecting the different emphasis in their diet upon feeding on other marine mammals from which they would want to remain undetected. The resident pods feed primarily upon Pacific salmon and are much more vocal. Their calls tend to be shared by all members of the group, and are highly stable for periods which may exceed ten years. Since members of different pods can also show some similarity in calls, it is thought that these pods may have common ancestry. These have been termed 'clans' and those comprising the greatest number of pods have the richest repertoires and are therefore thought to be the greatest age. When new pods bud off in this way from an ancestral group, they take with them certain stereotyped calls, but may also both lose calls and evolve new ones.

DOLPHIN INTELLIGENCE

The enormous interest in dolphins exhibited by many humans has invariably led to comparisons with ourselves, and speculations that dolphins are highly intelligent. Is this true, and, indeed, what do we mean by intelligence anyway?

Dictionary definitions of intelligence refer to 'powers of intellect, reasoning or understanding (apprehension, insight or abstract thought)'. A person with particular quickness of understanding is viewed as more intelligent than others. However, we also apply the term in comparing one species of animal with another — amongst mammals, we consider humans more intelligent than chimpanzees, whilst we consider both more intelligent than a sheep, for example. Although there are more objective measures of intelligence, the comparisons most people make on a day-to-day basis invariably relate other animal species to themselves.

Dolphins look friendly, and the best known species 'smile' all the time (they cannot help it!). These are positive attributes in our eyes, and are often confused with intelligence. Indeed, in various parts of the world it would appear to be rather unintelligent to approach humans since dolphins are as likely as not to be slaughtered for food.

There are many eye-witness accounts of dolphins coming to each other's aid, and sometimes to the aid of other species, including even humans. This altruistic (selfless, sometimes self-sacrificial) behaviour is also viewed by us in a very positive light and confused with intelligence. It can be misplaced: for example, a dolphin may support a calf on its head for some considerable time after the death of that calf, presumably to help it to breathe. Furthermore, many other animals show altruistic behaviour which are not otherwise considered particularly intelligent. These include several species of birds (such as bee-eaters, Florida scrub jay and anis) which breed co-operatively and collectively incubate eggs or help feed young at the nest; and various social insects such as the honey-bee which also nest collectively with division of labour to include even sterile worker bees.

We have seen in earlier chapters how dolphins have become supremely adapted for life in an aquatic environment where sound is the main form of communication. They are so very different to us that we can scarcely imagine how their lives are organized, let alone the thought processes within their heads. And yet this is what we attempt to do when talking of intelligence in dolphins. We project our own ideas upon those of other animals, making direct comparisons with ourselves.

One method for studying the capacity for intelligence has been to examine the anatomy of the brain, in particular its size and the development of those parts attributed to learning. If one compares the sizes of brain of different species of mammal, primates generally have the largest brains (relative to body size), and the largest within primates are humans. Brain size is compared to body size for a given species because as animals become larger so do their brains. Dolphins also have relatively large brains. The weight of the brain as a percentage of body weight varies in dolphins between 0.25 and 1.5, compared with 1.9 percent in humans. Most of the brain is involved with non-intellectual processes like motor co-ordination, and so a better indication might be a comparison of the relative sizes of the neo-cortex, the surface grey matter part of

Bottle-nosed dolphin 'smiling'.

the brain with which we create, innovate and reason. This portion covers 98 per cent of the dolphin's cortex, a higher percentage even than humans. On the other hand, it is much thinner than in humans, and if one looks at other features related to intellectual processes such as the extent of folding of this grey matter, the degree to which it is differentiated into zones, and the density of neurones, we find a great deal of variation between different dolphin species with no particular pattern.

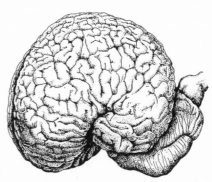

Dolphin brain.

A commonly used anatomical measure of potential mental abilities between species is the encephalization quotient (EQ), the ratio of brain volume to body surface area. These show an increase both evolutionarily (through the fossil record) and between living groups, from 1.5 in a **river dolphin** to 5.6 in the **bottle-nosed dolphin**. Within primates, the EQ of humans is around 7.4, and the chimpanzee around 2.5; almost all other mammals are much lower than 2.0. However, as yet we do not know enough about the make-up of the brain to be confident of precisely what these anatomical features reflect. The cetacean species with the highest EQs are all social dolphins, and it has been speculated that these brain developments may relate to the processing of acoustic information, particularly for the cognitive skills that a group-living existence may necessitate.

Current research effort is concentrating upon careful studies of dolphins in captivity, with particular emphasis upon their powers of communication by sound, possibilities for use of some form of language, and an ability to learn tasks and be innovative. The results so far have highlighted their capacity to imitate and learn sound signals through observation, both extremely rapidly and with great accuracy. They also have a well developed acoustic memory (but a relatively poor visual memory, unlike primates) with a capacity for forming, generalizing and learning rules, for both forming and acting upon abstract concepts, and for self-monitoring and regulation of their own behaviour. Although there are marked similarities in the cognitive characteristics of dolphins and those of some great apes like the chimpanzee, we must be cautious before extrapolating from captive studies when considering dolphin intellect.

In conclusion, although information seems to be processed in much the same way for dolphins and primates, and this may explain some similarities in brain development, they also show important differences. Dolphins appear unable to represent their world in purely visual terms, and all attempts to demonstrate the existence of a natural language have been unsuccessful. On the other hand, they do show great cognitive flexibility, being able to relate information between sound and visual cues. A dolphin can rapidly recognize an object visually that it previously experienced solely acoustically, and conversely, can recognize an object acoustically that previously it had only experienced visually. We still have much to discover about the ways that dolphins make use of their sensory capabilities.

Obtaining a mate

For a dolphin to be able to reproduce successfully, it must first make contact with a potential mate. If a species is relatively solitary, and lives in a wide expanse of relatively uniform sea, a good way of doing this is to have regular and predictable temporary social gatherings.

Many of the large baleen whales undergo extensive seasonal migrations and have traditional feeding and breeding grounds which they usually visit either annually or biennially. In this way, the chances of finding a mate are maximized. Site faithfulness and seasonality seem to be the main ways in which whales can find a mate. Although most dolphin species are also seasonal breeders, they may roam over large areas in pursuit of ever-moving prey, without following any particular migration route. One advantage of living in groups is that they have more opportunity to mate with a female in oestrus.

The majority of dolphin species give birth 10-12 months after mating. This provides the opportunity for some synchrony of breeding based on the seasons. In temperate and polar regions in particular, there is strong seasonality in food abundance. In the North Atlantic, for example, food is relatively scarce during the winter months and peaks in abundance during mid or late summer. This probably explains why many species of dolphin in the region form large aggregations during the summer, and give birth sometime between April and September. In late summer, as calves grow and become more independent, and when food is often at peak abundance, there is generally an increase in social activity, with observations of dolphins mating with one another. For most species this will not involve those females that have given birth in the current year, although in the case of **harbour porpoises**, individuals have been found simultaneously lactating and bearing a foetus.

The presence of a ready supply of food presumably makes it easier for dolphins to devote a higher portion of the day to other activities such as socializing. Delphinids like the **bottle-nosed dolphin** live in large social networks where males maintain social contact in the areas/groups in which they were born, but can wander from one group to another to gain mating access to unrelated females.

Bottle-nosed dolphins mating.

Some species have longer gestation (i.e. pregnancy) periods (around 14-17 months), making it more difficult to synchronize activities on a seasonal basis. Examples are **pilot whales** and the **killer whale**. Studies of their social structure indicate that they form stable groups with males apparently being strongly bonded with their mothers. Females also tend to remain within the groups in which they were born, but in order to promote outbreeding (gene exchange between unrelated groups), mixing can occur where males from a group temporarily leave their mothers to mate with receptive females in other groups. Such transient groupings have been observed in **long-finned pilot whales** during the month of March from weatherships that spend the year in the north-east Atlantic; and in the closely studied **killer whales** of Puget Sound, British Columbia.

Once sexually mature, a male dolphin has a fairly simple annual sexual cycle. Adult females, on the other hand, rarely have the opportunity to conceive in successive years, because there is usually a period of rest between the end of lactation and the next ovulation. Some females can become pregnant whilst still suckling the previous calf, but during pregnancy, they cannot ovulate so that during this period they will not be receptive to potential mates. Although in some species, ovulation may take place soon after giving birth, where suckling is prolonged, it usually occurs towards the end of lactation. Indeed, increasing evidence is accumulating to suggest that the period between conceptions may be quite lengthy. Observations of recognizable individuals, for example, have indicated that female **killer whales** give birth at intervals of between three and eight years, whilst **bottle-nosed dolphin** females breed every three to six years. The reason for this lengthy delay between calving may be primarily social, relating to the need for an extended period of maternal care, with the development of a strong bond between mother and calf.

Oestrus occurs when one or more eggs are released from ripe follicles in the ovaries, and pass into the uterus where they are available for fertilization by the sperm of a male. In tropical waters where there is little difference in the seasons, ovulations in some species may occur during most months of the year. However, in the majority of cases (and particularly at high latitudes), there is some seasonality of ovulations and hence births.

Courtship is an important prelude to successful mating. During this process, there may be some mate choice on the part of one or both sexes. Information is also relayed to show that the two partners belong to the same species, they are of the appropriate sex, and they are both reproductively active.

The readiness of females to mate may be relayed by various cues, such as changes in the shape and colour of the genital area, possible discharge of hormones in the faeces or urine, and certain behavioural actions which may also involve sound cues. Both **bottle-nosed dolphins** and **harbour porpoises**, for example, produce pulsed yelps during courtship.

Courtship may take various forms ranging from chases to flipper contact, simultaneous surfacing to extravagant breaching. When courtship is leading to mating, it usually involves belly contact, with the male gliding beneath the female or, in some cases, the female turning belly up just beneath the surface and the male passing over her. Actual coition occurs in the same way as other mammals, with the penis of the male (which can be pretty large!) being inserted into the vagina of the female so that the semen containing millions of sperms can be delivered into the urethra where it enters the uterus for fertilization of the single egg. Mating may be repeated several times by an individual male, although for many dolphin species, we believe that a female is mated successively by several males. In those cases, males will be competing to deliver as much sperm as possible close to the ova, and those with longer penises will have an advantage by displacing or diluting the sperm of other males within the female.

During attempts between males to gain access to females, there may be aggressive interactions, and a dominance hierarchy can develop, with subordinates (often younger males) denied access to the adult females in the group. Younger animals in particular may have extensive scarring caused by the tooth rake marks of other males. This may be why the males of some whale species (for example the **sperm whale**, and the **beaked whales**) have visible teeth whereas females and young do not. The strikingly elongated tooth of the **narwhal** may serve this function since observations have been made of males engaging in aggressive behaviour, scarring one another with their tusks during jousting contests (see illustration p. 51). In those situations more than two males may participate, and, during these duels, it is thought that a dominance hierarchy is established, much as has been observed in other dolphins. The tips of tusks are sometimes found embedded in the head or the broken end of a tusk of a captured male so these duels can have quite serious consequences. It is presumed that the most successful males during the duels are the most powerful and fittest individuals, whose genes would contribute best to the fitness of a female's offspring. Whether or not the most successful males do mate with more females, and whether these in turn yield fitter offspring, has not yet been established.

Rearing a calf

Once successful fertilization has taken place, an egg is implanted in the wall of one or other of the two uterine horns (depending on which ovary released the egg). Occasionally two eggs may be fertilized at the same time, giving rise to twins, but multiple foetuses are very rare and almost invariably die before birth, so that, unlike many other mammals, cetaceans give birth to only one young at a time.

During pregnancy, the foetus grows relatively slowly at first but much more rapidly in the latter half, nourished by the placenta of its mother. By the time of birth, the foetus, which has been fully formed for a few months, is 30-40 per cent the length of its parent. The growth spurt in the months prior to birth is important because when the calf is born, it enters a much colder environment (sea temperatures usually less than 25°C, and in polar seas, near freezing) than its mother's womb (around 37°C). Indeed, with some of the smaller dolphin species like the **harbour porpoise**, it is thought that some mortality occurs because their small surface area to volume ratio has caused them to lose too much heat and die through hypothermia if born too early. This may be an important reason why for those species such as the harbour porpoise, living in relatively cool waters, there is strong seasonality in births, which occur mainly in midsummer.

In dolphins, calves are usually born tail first. They are quickly assisted to the surface for their first breaths, and the mother then remains very close to its young one, for a period that can vary from weeks to months. During birth, the mother may be attended by other dolphins, usually non-pregnant females which are sometimes referred to as 'aunts'. These have been observed on occasions assisting the mother in taking the calf to the surface, by supporting it from underneath and even helping the mother herself in this way if she is in any difficulty.

During the period immediately surrounding birth, non-pregnant females may show a great interest in the mother-calf pair, and follow them closely. Generally at this time, dolphin communities split up into small groups or even become

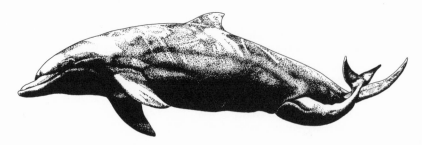

Birth of a calf.

solitary. Nursery groups may form between mother-calf pairs (with or without 'aunts') and during this time they are often segregated from males which play little part in parental care.

Throughout the early period of life the calf maintains a position very close to its mother, usually above the midline forward of the dorsal fin. The calf's flipper may actually be pressed against her side so gaining assistance during movement without resulting in much increase in energy expenditure on the part of the mother.

Nourishment for the calf comes from the energy-rich milk of the mother which may contain anywhere between 16 and 37 per cent fat (even higher amongst some baleen whales) compared with that of human milk which is 3-5 per cent fat.

The mother suckles the calf by squirting milk directly into its mouth when the infant grips the corner of her nipple (in most cases, it cannot suck in the same way as other mammals because the lips are not manoeuvrable). The calf is fully dependent upon its mother's milk for at least four months, although, in at least some species, other females may also suckle the young one. Studies of **pilot whales** have indicated that these include old females that are no longer reproducing but which can still serve an important function in the group by assisting mothers in the care of their young.

Almost immediately after birth, female **bottle-nosed dolphins** have been observed to whistle nearly continuously for several days. This is thought to enable the calf to become strongly imprinted acoustically on its parent. The early whistles of the calf are relatively uniform but then acquire a more unique 'signature', which possibly serves for individual recognition.

The bond between mother and calf is very strong at first but then weakens as the calf grows older. Not only does the youngster make longer forays from its mother's side but it also starts to hunt for itself, and will take solid food long before it ceases suckling altogether. Indeed, at least for some species, for example the **pilot whales** and **killer whale,** occasional suckling may continue for several years.

One of the reasons why in some areas various species appear to show seasonal inshore movements into relatively shallow waters may be to enable calves of a few months' age to feed for themselves without having to dive too deeply.

During the period when a calf is becoming independent of its mother (which varies between species from anywhere between two or three months and a year or more), other behavioural changes may often be observed. Interactions with other young increase, to the extent that they can form segregated groups comprising individuals of the same age, and in some cases the same sex. For **killer whales, pilot whales, bottle-nosed dolphin** and **harbour porpoise,** these are generally of the same sex, usually male. For **spinner dolphin** and **dusky dolphin,** these are more usually of mixed sex. Aggressive interactions and play between young ones also increase as the calf grows older. The former probably serves partly to establish dominance hierarchies, whilst the latter provides the opportunity to acquire and develop the skills that are so necessary for finding food and avoiding predation, and which can mean the difference between life and death.

Spotted dolphin calf suckling mother.

Hawaiian spotted dolphin leaping.

Life History

The fortunes of dolphin populations of any particular species are dictated by two prime forces — reproduction and mortality. The longer that individuals live and the more young they produce, the greater the number of individuals there will be in the population. In a stable population one animal dies for every one that is born. If the birth rate exceeds the death rate, as in many human populations, they will increase in number. If the death rate is higher than the rate of births, the converse is true and the population will decline. This is the scenario facing a number of animal species, and is the subject of attention by conservationists concerned with preventing the extinction of species.

The age at which an individual starts to reproduce can vary both between and within species. Those dolphin species such as the **franciscana** and the **harbour porpoise**, with a lifespan of 15 or 20 years, may start reproducing when they are 2 to 4 years old, with little evidence of a difference between males and females. The **short-finned pilot whale** and **killer whale**, on the other hand, may live for 60 years or more. For them, reproduction starts when they are 9-16 years old. They also show a sexual difference. Female **short-finned pilot whales** start to breed at around 9 years old (range 7-12) whereas males do not do so until 16 years old. Female **killer whales** first breed when 8-10 years old but males are 15-16 years old before they breed. These sexual differences are presumably due to the fact that females are not competing, whereas young males have to compete with older males for females. If dominance hierarchies have already been established, this will make it even more difficult for young males to obtain a successful mating. For several species of social dolphins, such as **common**, **striped** and **bottle-nosed dolphin**, there seems to be little difference between the sexes in the age at which they first reproduce. Perhaps for them, males move around much more readily between groups, and long-standing bonds between males and groups of females are scarce.

The determination of the age at which individuals are sexually mature is not straightforward, and requires the use of various fairly sophisticated techniques. For female dolphins, sexual maturity is assessed by internal examination of dead animals for the presence of evidence of at least one ovulation, whether or not it has led to pregnancy. This involves looking for the presence of a corpus luteum, the mass of tissue which is left after ovulation when a mature follicle ruptures from the ovary. It persists only when fertilization leading to pregnancy has occurred; otherwise, it regresses to form a scar-like corpus albicans.

For males, it is rather more difficult to be certain when sexual maturity has been reached. The usual criterion used is the size of the testis which increases in weight at this time. However, additional information which it is useful to collect includes a measurement of the diameter of the testis tubule, and histological examination to detect the presence of sperm and spermatogenesis.

Having established that an individual is sexually mature, the next problem is to estimate its age. In toothed whales (the dolphins that are the subject of this book), this is achieved by taking out a tooth, sectioning it with a microtome (a very finely cutting guillotine), and then, under a microscope, counting the growth layers either in the dentine or the cementum (see drawing). They usually appear as one narrow translucent and one broader opaque lamination, which for a number of species is considered to represent an annual growth layer. However, it is not always easy to distinguish different layers, and this can result in observers obtaining different counts from the same material. One way to check this has been to inject tetracycline into living dolphins whilst they are immature. The tetracycline is then deposited in the growing dentine and may be detected subsequently under ultra-violet light. If the animal is re-captured a certain number of years later, the period elapsed can be related to the additional number of growth layers observed. The result of such studies on **bottle-nosed dolphins**, for example, have supported the idea that two laminations are laid down annually.

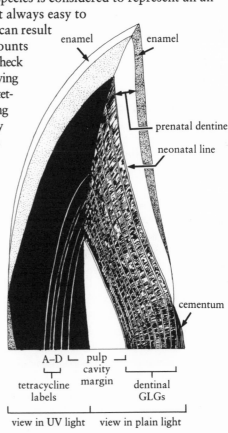

However, there is a need to repeat these studies on other species because there may be differences. The development of two alternate layers, a narrow one and a broader one, reflects the seasonality in diet that many dolphin species experience. If food quality and quantity ingested varies little through the year, alternate layers may not appear clearly. In fact, the relationship between deposition of dentine layers and feeding conditions can provide useful information about the health of an individual or population. Anomalous pat-

Diagram of thin section of tooth from hypothetical dolphin, sowing tetracycline labels, A-D under ultra-violet light (left-hand side) and dentinal growth layer group layering patterns under plain light (right-hand side).

terns of deposition of minerals have been observed in a number of species, and increasingly can be related to environmental changes and to life history events. Such anomalies can include pulp stones, marker lines, interference in regular deposition of minerals, reabsorption of the dentine and disturbances to lines in the cementum. Marker lines, for example, appear regularly in **short-finned pilot whale** teeth, within a short time of them being taken into captivity. In harbour porpoises, marker lines occur frequently at 2-4 years of age, the usual age of sexual maturation. It is believed that this phenomenon may be linked to stress and/or nutritional problems experienced by individuals at the time.

Movements and the annual cycle

A number of species of baleen whale undergo extensive seasonal migrations from polar regions, where food is abundant, to equatorial regions where, although food is often scarce, sea temperatures are much warmer. For those species, summer is generally spent feeding nearer the poles whilst breeding occurs during winter towards the equator.

Dolphins do not show the same latitudinal migrations, but they may still move over large areas in the course of an average year. As with the baleen whales, their movements are linked to the need to find suitable areas for breeding and then, once the calf is born, areas that are relatively abundant with food so that their calves can grow quickly and they themselves can recover from the stress placed upon them (or, at least, the females) during breeding. Once they have recovered, their calves have become more independent, and there is sufficient food for them to take time off for other activities, they may devote more time to social and sexual behaviour, including mating.

The areas over which river dolphins may range appear to be determined greatly by water flow and the rise and fall of water levels in rivers which are controlled by seasonal rains. The **Ganges** and **Indus susus** are usually confined to the main river channels in the dry season, but with the rains, they disperse into tributaries and swollen creeks. The South American **boto** and Chinese **baiji** both do likewise, the latter even entering lakes during spring floods.

Killer whale pods also have large home ranges which in Puget Sound off the north-west Pacific coast, where they have been studied since 1976, may extend over 200 to 300 miles (320 to 480 km). Even during a single day they have been recorded regularly travelling 75 to 100 miles (120 to160 km) whilst foraging for food. Similar extensive ranging behaviour is starting to be recorded in killer whale communities elsewhere in the world. For example, a pod of eight killer whales was followed over a period of twelve hours one August day in 1993 for almost 50 miles (75 km) down the east coast of the Outer Hebrides in north-west Scotland.

Dusky dolphin.

Information about ranging movements requires that individual animals should be recognizable. This has either relied upon photo-identification of uniquely marked individuals, as with the Puget Sound killer whales and various smaller dolphins, or the attachment of radio transmitters to the animal which is then tracked from land, boat, plane or even satellite. Indeed, some of the most extraordinary results have come from recent studies carried out by the British zoologist, Tony Martin, in conjunction with Canadian biologists, who, by satellite radio-tracking, found that **white whales** can travel over three thousand kilometres, often at depths exceeding 600 metres under almost impenetrable pack ice, between the Beaufort Sea (east Canadian Arctic) and Wrangel Island, Russia.

Spinner dolphins in Hawaii, studied by the American cetologist Ken Norris and his colleagues, spent most of their time close to the coast, but might still range up to 30 miles (50 km) from day to day. However, they would rarely move further than 60 miles (100 km) away.

Dusky dolphins, studied by the American zoologists Bernd and Melany Würsig in southern Argentina, ranged over an area of approximately 600 square miles (1,500 sq. km). During the hours of darkness they appeared to be at rest, making only slow movements and occurring in small groups of 6-15 animals no more than half a mile from the shore. In the morning, they then moved into deeper waters between 1 and 6 miles from shore, where they would fan out in a line abreast with each animal about 10 metres from the next. In this way, they are able to cover an area of sea up to 150 metres wide in search of food. Once food is found, groups coalesce to form aggregations of up to 300 dolphins. By mid-afternoon, feeding may be concentrated in one area, and increasing time is spent in social and sexual activity.

Sharing southern Argentinian waters are **bottle-nosed dolphins**, and here,

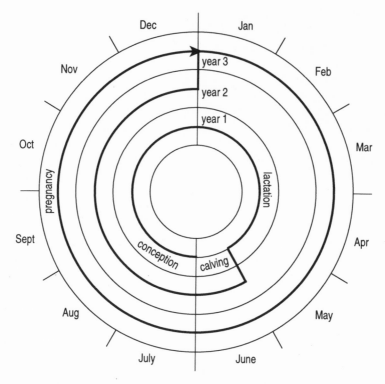

Annual cycle of common dolphin over a three-year period.

individuals tracked by the Würsigs sometimes moved about 180 miles (300 km) over a short period of time before returning to the same location. In Florida, the individual home ranges of bottle-nosed dolphins were generally much smaller, varying from 5 to15 square miles (15 to 40 sq. km).

The extent to which individuals move around both in the short and long term very probably depends upon the quantity of suitable food available to them and its dispersion. We might therefore expect home ranges for a particular species to vary between regions, and for species differences also to exist. Those populations and species that are generally coastal appear to have smaller home ranges, at least in the short term. A **harbour porpoise** radio-tracked over a four-day period in New Brunswick, eastern Canada, travelled at least 25 miles (40 km), though rarely more than 12 miles (20 km) within a day. During a 24-hour period, three-quarters of the time was spent apparently foraging or feeding. This is a much higher proportion of time than for many other species studied, for example **killer whale** and **bot-**

tle-nosed dolphin. It may account at least in part for the comparatively non-social behaviour of this species since it presumably can devote only a small portion of time to social activities.

In those parts of the world where there are marked seasons, dolphins do tend to make more extensive movements. In Arctic waters, in autumn, **white whales** and **narwhal** start to move south, giving rise to aggregations on migration in localities like Lancaster Sound (eastern Canada) that may number thousands of animals. Winter is spent in ice-free areas like the Davis Strait, Hudson Bay, Greenland Sea and Barents Sea. Sometimes individuals stray further afield and occasional sightings occur off the coasts of Newfoundland and various North Sea countries. For those species, like several other toothed whales, mating mainly occurs during those periods when they are gathered into large groups. Because **narwhals** and **white whale** have relatively long gestation periods (14 to15 months), if the calves are to gain the benefit of the late summer peak in food abundance, they must mate during late winter or spring, presumably just prior to or during the mass migration to those areas that were ice-locked through the winter.

Causes of death

In a world where humans by their actions impose a major impact on animals including dolphins, it is necessary to distinguish mortality caused by humans, either directly or indirectly, from other causes of death which we refer to as 'natural' mortality. We shall consider the effects of humans upon dolphins in the next chapter. In this chapter, the three main causes of 'natural' mortality — predation, parasitism and disease — will be reviewed.

Besides humans, the main predators of dolphins are sharks and **killer whales**, but **false killers**, **pygmy killers** and possibly **pilot whales** are all thought to prey upon them at least occasionally. Opportunities for observing direct predation in the wild are rare, and most evidence comes from the regular presence of tooth scars on a variety of dolphin species. Not all scars are made by potential predators, however. Adult males of most dolphin species may rake one another with their teeth whilst fighting for mating access to females. In those cases, the scar lines are usually parallel and close together, caused by the rows of teeth in the dolphin jaw. Round or oval lacerations with radiating groove patterns are characteristic of a tropical shark called *Isistius brasiliensis* which attaches itself by means of its suction-like lips. For a long time they were thought to be wounds made by lampreys. Sometimes, dolphins may be wounded by their prey: circular scars found on **pilot whales**, **Risso's dolphins** and some other species are often the result of attachment by the suckers on the tentacles of squid upon which they feed.

Although it is difficult to determine how important predators are in caus-

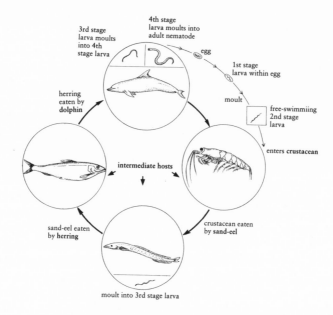

3rd stage larva moults into 4th stage larva

4th stage larva moults into adult nematode

egg

1st stage larva within egg

moult

free-swimmiing 2nd stage larva

herring eaten by dolphin

enters crustacean

intermediate hosts

crustacean eaten by sand-eel

sand-eel eaten by herring

moult into 3rd stage larva

Life cycle of typical dolphin nematode parasite.

ing mortality, examination of dolphins and whales of various species has indicated that anywhere between 3 and 18 per cent of individuals may show signs of shark attack. The behaviour of several dolphin species also shows adaptations to minimize the chances of attack by sharks or **killer whales.** They may form larger groups with mothers and calves in the centre and adult males between them and the potential predator. When killer whales are in the vicinity, dolphins have also been observed to become silent, presumably to avoid detection.

Dolphins are well known to have a wide variety of parasites. Most of the time they do not have any serious detrimental effect. Indeed, if they did, it would usually be a disadvantage to the parasite, since the untimely death of the host would remove a home and/or source of nourisment for the parasite, and in most cases terminate opportunities for it to pass to the next stage of its life cycle.

In the bottle-nosed dolphin, there is a lungworm called *Halocercus lagenorhynchi* which has been found even in the foetus. In most cases, however, rates of parasitism are low for newborn dolphins, but build up as they grow older. Although adults may have comparatively large burdens of parasites inside them, it appears to be a combination of factors such as food shortage, physiological stress, viral or bacterial disease and pollutant contamination that enables parasites to proliferate and have a significant effect.

When death comes, it is often difficult to know which of these was ultimately responsible.

Nematodes that reside apparently innocuously in lungs and stomach can, under circumstances of food shortage or some other stressful condition, overwhelm the host. Various species of nematode inhabit the bronchi of the lungs whilst those of the genus *Crassicauda* infest the kidneys and urino-genital system, where it may cause congestion of the liver and consequent renal failure. Infection by *Crassicauda* has also been linked to mortality of young pantropical **spotted dolphins** by causing damage to the bones of the head. In the latter case, this was estimated to amount to between one and three per cent of total annual mortality of this species. The invasion of the mammary glands by another closely related nematode was thought to be responsible for reproductive failure in **Atlantic white-sided dolphins** The tiny nematode *Stenurus* which lives normally in the respiratory tract is commonly also found in the auditory or eustachian tubes, middle ears and cranial sinuses. Tapeworms occupy the digestive tract, and trematodes (exclusively in the adult phase) occur in the liver, gall bladder, brain, lung and intestine.

In recent years, there have been cases of mass mortality amongst marine mammals (dolphins, whales and seals). In 1990, an outbreak of morbillivirus infection led to the death of at least 750 **striped dolphins** in the Mediterranean. These also were heavily infested by parasites and had high levels of pollutants which could have contributed to a lowered resistance to disease. Sometimes, toxins produced by marine plankton can lead to mortality. Brevetoxin produced by the dinoflagellate *Gymnodinium breve* was implicated in the mass mortality of some 750 **bottle-nosed dolphins** along the East Coast of the United States in 1987-88.

Several whale species have barnacles, copepod and amphipod crustaceans

Commerson's dolphin.

(the latter called 'whale lice') attached to their skin, particularly around the head, on the flippers and tail flukes. Dolphins usually travel too fast for these to remain attached on them in any numbers, although stalked barnacles (cirripeds) of the genus *Conchoderma* may settle on teeth where they are exposed for example by a crooked, healed fracture of the jaw. Another cirriped *Xenobalanus globicipitis* may be found attached to the edge of the flippers or tail flukes on a variety ~~of dolphins including~~ ~~striped and bottle-~~ nosed dolphins, long-fi~~n~~ ~~, and~~ even killer whale. The whale louse *Isocyamus delphi*~~ii~~ ~~occurs~~ on the skin of dolphins, in natural openings and wounds.

STRANDINGS

Most news items ab~~out dol~~phins relate to incidents when they come ashore, either alive or dead. ~~When~~ a dolphin dies, it will first sink, but as it fills with gases, it may becom~~e disl~~odged from the seabed and float to the surface. Here it will remain for a p~~eriod~~ of time either decomposing slowly or being attacked and eaten by scaven~~ging s~~eabirds. Eventually, most of these carcasses probably sink to the bottom ~~and~~ start to disintegrate and may never be seen again. A small proportion, ~~howev~~er, will be carried by winds and onshore currents towards the coast w~~here th~~ey may be washed ashore. Most of these strandings involve single indi~~vidual~~s, although, sometimes, storms can bring a number of dead animals to th~~e coa~~st over a short period.

The reasons for li~~ve ani~~mals beaching themselves continue to tax the minds of scientists, and, despite m~~any th~~eories, we do not know if one or a few of the various possible reasons put forward are mainly responsible. Indeed, it may well be that there *is* a variety of causes for live strandings, depending upon the circumstance.

Most single live strandings appear to be the result of injury or illness, and when it occurs, the animal almost invariably dies. Sometimes, that animal may be accompanied by another (its parent or offspring, perhaps its mate or some other associate), and when it comes ashore, the other stays close by, often showing signs of obvious distress, with much whistling and high frequency clicks made by both individuals.

Occasionally (and it is in fact a rare event), many individuals may come ashore together. Such mass-strandings tend to involve certain species, such as **pilot whale, false killer whale, white-sided dolphin** and **sperm whale**. These are all typically gregarious, living in deep waters usually far from shore. They also usually show bonding between individuals within the group so that if one individual strands, others are likely to follow. But what brings them close to the coast in the first place?

Some pelagic species, such as the **white-sided dolphin, pilot whale** and **killer whale**, follow their prey inshore. In the Northern Isles and Hebrides of North Scotland, it is not unusual for any of these species to travel up the long deep

Mass stranding of pilot whales.

fjords, remaining close to land for days or even weeks. During this period, they cause much concern to local people that they may be in difficulties, but usually they eventually return to sea again. Although dolphins and whales do follow prey inshore, when a mass stranding occurs, there is often no evidence for feeding having taken place just beforehand and so it is not thought to play a major role in these events.

Some theories seem unlikely and are untestable. They include the notion that dolphins may seek safety on land during periods of stress, returning to the primeval condition of their ancestors. Or that they strand whilst attempting to follow ancient migratory routes. Or that mass strandings are a means of population regulation during periods of high population density. Or simply that they are committing suicide as humans do occasionally. All these ideas imply some purpose, either conscious or instinctive, and are not of any selective advantage or they invoke the concept of group selection (where selection operates at a groups level rather than at the level of the gene). Most of them are impossible to test adequately and have little if any evidence to support them.

One recent theory that has been proposed relates to the fact that some cetaceans, for example **common dolphins** and **pygmy sperm whales**, apparently have tiny particles of magnetite in the soft tissue covering the brain, similiar to those found in other vertebrates that use the magnetic field for orientation. As yet, no species of animal has been proven to possess a magnetic map sense that would identify its actual position. A review by Margaret Klinowska of the sites of live strandings on the coasts of Britain found that they tended to occur where the north-south magnetic contours of the ocean floor intersect land perpendicularly, particularly in areas of geomagnetic lows. She postulated that animals were misinterpreting geomagnetic information and coming ashore. However, attempts to find similar correlations on other continents have been less successful, and the only experimental study with cetaceans, involving two **bottle-nosed dolphins,** failed to show any response to changes in a magnetic field or its intensity.

Whatever the reason for coming close to shore, it is the actual phenomenon of stranding that is difficult to resolve. Some animals become trapped and ground themselves on an incoming tide, in areas of complicated coastal topography or oceanographic conditions — these may involve long meandering channels, broad tidal flats, strong or unusual currents, or extreme tidal flow or volume such as may occur during spring tides near full or new moon. A few of these animals may manage to refloat themselves and swim away on the next tide.

One proposal that has frequently been made in connection with live strandings is that the distortion of echolocation signals in shallow water may provide false clues. This would occur particularly in areas of gently sloping beaches, or when the sea is churned by air and sand during storms. The failure of dolphin sonar in orientation and navigation may also result from neurological disease or parasites affecting their hearing. A recent study of stranded small cetaceans in California by William Walker and colleagues found brain lesions in 39 out of 43 animals, caused by the trematode *Nasitrema.* Their effects on the air sinuses, inner ear and brain were considered to be the major cause of stranding. Heavy nematode infections of the ear and the acoustic sinuses, thought to affect either their sonar abilities or sense of balance, have also been found in stranded specimens of a variety of cetacean species. Although a few studies of mass-strandings have shown evidence of illness amongst several individuals in the group, and others have found individuals showing potentially debilitating effects of long-standing disease, there have been other occasions when it has been difficult to attribute illness, disease or parasitism to the mass stranding.

On coming ashore, dolphins are likely to experience physiological stress and shock, and maybe also actual physical damage. Attempts to rescue them must take this into account. Any action towards re-floating needs to be co-operative, and should, where possible, involve a veterinarian or other qualified person. The dolphins should be held in shallow water until all the live animals have been refloated, and then released as a single group, aligned towards the open sea and making best use of the tide. Before this, any stranded dolphin must be kept moist and cool, using cloths soaked in sea water over the back (but not the blowhole). It may also need some physical support so that vital organs are not crushed, or if the animal has to be moved back into the water (do not roll the animal). This can be achieved by lifting on a stretcher, or gentle dragging with wide, well-padded slings under the body behind the flippers (and if necessary, under the head). Sadly, in many situations the most humane action will be euthanasia, administered by a veterinarian or other qualified professional.

Dolphin and girl statue at London Bridge.

• 6 •

Dolphins and Man

Our relationship with dolphins is an ambiguous one. In some parts of the world, we revere them — they are amongst the most popular animals; in other regions, they are routinely exploited for food or killed for their perceived threat to human activities such as fishing. Neither of these approaches to dolphins is new: they date back centuries into the mists of time. The notion that humans have moved only recently from an attitude of considering them essentially as a food resource with various by-products to an attitude of respect and admiration may apply to whales but not to dolphins. They have figured highly in folklore and mythology dating back to prehistoric Arctic peoples and others like the Ancient Greeks.

This difference in attitude to whales and dolphins is probably due to the relative ease with which at least some species of whales could be hunted and the extent to which they could support local communities in food, clothing and other products. Before engine power, dolphins were generally too swift to be pursued by boats, and in only a few areas was it possible to drive them ashore. Another reason may have been the observation of occasional altruistic acts, with dolphins coming to each other's aid, and even, according to legend, rescuing humans. Coupled with their often coastal habits, apparent friendly interest in boats, and a facial expression that misled people into thinking that they were smiling at them, they are more inclined to be viewed positively than negatively.

Hunting

The earliest record of dolphins being hunted comes from carvings in Norse stone age settlements dating back 4,000 years, although bones from various whale species were found in kitchen middens of Alaskan eskimos, Canadian Inuits and other Arctic peoples between 5,000 and 8,000 years ago. In those days it is likely that most small cetaceans were either trapped amongst ice floes or were driven ashore. In both cases, early methods probably made use of canoes with one or more paddles, a harpoon usually with line and float attached, and a lance or two for final killing of the animal and pulling ashore. Broadly similar methods have been used in several different parts of the world for centuries with little modification.

At various times in our history, this method of driving has been adopted on tightly knit schools of **long-finned pilot whale** in the islands of North Scotland, the Faroe islands, Newfoundland and Cape Cod; along the coasts of Greenland for **narwhal** and **white whale;** and along the coasts of Japan, the Solomon islands and various other Pacific islands for various schooling dolphins mainly of the genus *Stenella*. Along the Pacific north-west coast, the Indians of Vancouver and Washington hunted **killer whales** (and larger species like the gray whale) using an enormous harpoon operated from large dug-out canoes. Farther north in the Bering Sea, the natives of the Aleutian Islands, Kamchatka Peninsula and the Kurile Islands used poisoned lances to kill their prey, which would then die at sea, drifting ashore a few days later.

In many parts of the world, dolphins continue to be taken in large numbers. A review by the International Whaling Commission in 1982 estimated that more than 100,000 dolphins, porpoises and small whales were being taken annually.

By far the greatest numbers were killed in Japanese coastal fisheries, generally for subsistence. An estimated 219,539 small cetaceans were killed between 1976 and 1987. Over 50 per cent of these were **Dall's porpoise** (with annual takes averaging nearly 10,000 animals; but 45,000 taken in 1988), killed with hand-held harpoons from small boats. Other species taken in significant numbers included (in descending order) **striped dolphin, spotted dolphin, bottle-nosed dolphin, short-finned pilot whale**, and **Pacific white-sided dolphin**. These are herded into shallow bays such as occur along the Izu and Kii Peninsulas, with escape routes blocked by nets. Fishermen then wade into the water and cut their throats using long knives.

In the Arctic, most hunting has a subsistence element, even if the meat and tusks may also be sold commercially. In eastern Canada and west Greenland, Inuit peoples hunt **narwhals**, eating the blubber (known as '*muktuk*') and some of the red meat, and, in west Greenland at least, feeding the remainder to their sled dogs. They also take the ivory tusks, although following European Community action, prices on the international markets were considerably reduced so that hunters received only around $150-300 per tusk whereas they had obtained an average of $900 prior to this, in 1982. Annual kills of narwhal during the 1980s ranged from around 250-400 in Canada and 150-650 in Greenland, with only about 100 tusks, in international trade each year. Numbers taken annually can vary greatly depending upon opportunistic kills of groups trapped in holes surrounded by freezing ice (these holes being referred to as '*savssats*').

The other main target species in the arctic is the **white whale** or **beluga**, again taken primarily by local people for their own use. Catches in the Soviet Union between 1900 and 1960 averaged 3,000-4,000 per year but nowadays around 400-1,000 are taken annually (all figures include estimated numbers killed but lost). Canadian natives take about 600-1,200 per year, and Alaskans about 200-400, whilst Greenland Inuits take an average of 800-1,000 per year. Netting, as occurs in some parts of the Soviet Union, results in lower losses than when they are harpooned or shot.

Greenland is the only country in the world presently reporting large direct catches of **harbour porpoise**, mainly used for human consumption. Catches

The Faroese drive pilot whales into shallow waters before killing them.

vary greatly between years but are in the order of 700-1,000 per year.

One of the most publicized local hunts occurs in the Faroe Islands where for many centuries **long-finned pilot whales** have been driven into bays, and then ashore where they are killed using a long knife called a 'gaff'. These drives are referred to as 'grinds'. The annual catch has fluctuated greatly over the years with peaks between 1720-40, 1820-50, and 1930-60 although in recent years the catches have also been high, averaging around 1-3,000 per year.

Elsewhere in the world, there are large directed catches of dolphins in South America, particularly Peru where up to 10,000 **dusky dolphins**, **common dolphins** and **Burmeister's porpoise** are killed annually either using nets or by harpooning. In southern Chile, fishermen catch particularly **Commerson's dolphins** and **Peale's dolphins**, but also **Burmeister's porpoise** for bait in the crab fishery and for meat. Over 4,000 were taken in 1978-9.

Smaller scale directed hunts occur in several other parts of the world. In the Caribbean small numbers of **spinner, spotted** and **bottle-nosed dolphins,** and **short-finned pilot whales** are taken opportunistically on the islands of St Vincent, St Lucia and Dominica. Other island-based hunts occur occasionally in the Azores (**long-finned pilot whales** and **common dolphins**) and the Solomon Islands and Papua New Guinea (**Fraser's, spotted** and **striped dolphins**). There is also limited hunting for **hump-backed dolphins** in the Red Sea, Arabian Sea and Persian Gulf; of **dusky** and **Heaviside's dolphins** on the South African coast; and **bottle-nosed dolphins** in Sri Lanka, West Africa, and Venezuela, generally for human consumption.

One of the largest dolphin fisheries that ever occurred was in the Black and Azov Seas where up to 250,000-300,000 animals (mainly **common dolphins** and **harbour porpoise**) were taken annually between 1931-41. Although the fishery was closed in 1967 in the Soviet Union, Romania and Bulgaria, the Turks continued and in 1973, almost 130,000 animals were reported killed. Turkey eventually ceased the hunt in 1983 after public pressure, but illegal killing, possibly on a large scale, still takes place.

Dolphins and fisheries

In several parts of the world, wild dolphins have been reported with humans in associations which are regarded as symbiotic, the two co-operating in some way, usually in pursuit of prey.

For at least thirty-five years (and possibly up to ninety years), during the last century, a **killer whale** called 'Old Tom' was sighted repeatedly off Eden, in Twofold Bay, Eastern Australia, with one or more groups of killer whale. They would traditionally enter the area before the northward migration of the right and humpback whales from southerly waters, and remain there for the June-November whaling season. During this period, the killers would co-operate with humans by chasing and attacking right whales. If they became entangled in the whalers' lines, the humans would free them, and the relationship was viewed, at least by the whalers, as symbiotic.

The Imragen, an ancient nomadic people from Mauritania, West Africa, numbering today only a few hundred, use a centuries-old coastal netting technique to capture fish. When mullet are schooling along an 80-mile (130 km) stretch of coast (between Cape Blanc and Cape Timiris), the fishermen move from site to site, awaiting the arrival of **Atlantic hump-backed dolphins** attracted by the beating of the sea surface with sticks. The dolphins then help the fishermen to herd fish into the nets and, in so doing, gain a meal themselves by trapping them against the nets. In Laguna, Brazil, **bottle-nosed dolphins** drive mullet towards fishermen, indicating to them with a stereotyped splash when they should throw their nets over the fish. This

Co-operative fishing in Mauritania.

system has operated almost daily for over one hundred years and, according to three generations of locals, has involved a single dolphin group out of a number in the area, with participation from the same female dolphins and their offspring. The entire fishing operation is initiated and controlled by the dolphins rather than the humans, but both benefit from the association.

Bottle-nosed dolphins also assist the natives of Moreton Bay, south-east Queensland, by herding mullet into nets. **Irrawaddy dolphins** in Burma, attracted by local fishermen oar-tapping on the sides of their boats, circle their nets to concentrate the fish which are then divided up between the humans and the dolphins. Other reports of co-operative fishing between man and dolphins include the **boto** in the Amazon river in Brazil, the **Ganges susu** in the riverine system of that name, in India, and the **baiji** in the Yangtse River in China.

Sadly, not all relationships between dolphins and fishermen have been friendly ones. The conflict that can exist between them takes two forms: deliberate kills by fishermen when they perceive dolphins as damaging their livelihood either by competing for their food or damaging their nets; and accidental entrapment in fishing gear leading to their suffocation.

Attempts to prevent dolphins harming fishing activities in some regions have involved systematic culls. Fishermen from Iki Island, on the west coast of Japan, began an organized culling of dolphins in 1976. Although the conflict between dolphins and the hook-and-line fishery for yellowtail tuna has been apparent since around 1910, repeated attempts to kill or drive away the dolphins were unsuccessful at preventing the conflict. The dolphins affect the fisheries by damaging gear, and taking caught fish, whilst they are also reported to disperse fish shoals and to cause them to cease feeding. The annual number of dolphins killed increased annually until 1980 when 1,819 were taken, but then declined to around 150 per year until 1982. The total numbers killed by then were 4,147 **bottle-nosed dolphins**, 953 **false killer whales**, 525 **Risso's dolphins**, and 466 **Pacific white-sided dolphins**. Although no effective solution to the problem has been found, fewer dolphins are present on the fishing grounds nowadays, and only occasional culls (by driving) occur. Stomach analysis revealed that yellowtail tuna was a major food only for the **false killer whale**, highlighting the often large gap between the perceived and actual threat posed by marine mammal predators.

In most cases, retaliation by fishermen probably has little effect upon local dolphin populations or on their supposed damage. However, in the Mediterranean, commercial purse-seine and trawl fisheries in Spain, Italy, Yugoslavia, Turkey, Israel, Malta, Algeria and Morocco have all perceived **common dolphins** as a threat. Both direct and incidental catches are thought to have contributed to a recent decline in numbers of this species in the western Mediterranean.

Although dolphins have on occasions been seen as a threat to fisheries, we often overlook the converse impact that fisheries may have on dolphin populations. The collapse of energy-rich herring stocks in the North Sea during the mid-1960s, after decades of over-exploitation by man, followed

Dead dusky dolphins in Peru.

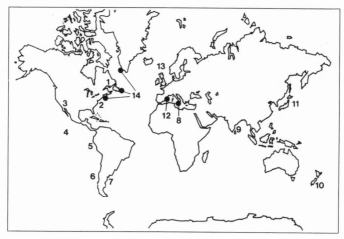

Map showing areas where major kills of dolphins have taken place.

1. Belugas in the St Lawrence Estuary now number only 3-400 and face current problems of chronic pollution

2. More than 700 bottle-nosed dolphins died along the east coast of the United States in 1987-8. Although cause of death was unknown, they are believed to have died partly as a result of consuming fish containing brevetoxin

3. The endangered vaquita is taken incidentally in gillnets set for totaba and other fish

4. Six million dolphins (spinner, common and spotted) have been estimated killed accidentally since 1960s in the tuna purse-seine fishery operating over the eastern tropical Pacific

5. Up to 10,000 small cetaceans (mainly dusky dolphin, Burmeister's porpoise, common dolphin, bottle-nosed dolphin and pilot whale) are killed each year both accidentally and deliberately in coastal waters of Peru

6. Several thousand dolphins and porpoises are harpooned annually for use as bait in the Chilean crab fishery

7. At least several hundred franciscanas and unknown numbers of dolphins of other species are killed annually in gillnet fisheries in northern Argentina. Unknown numbers have been incidentally killed also in Uruguay and Brazil

8. Unknown numbers (but possibly in low thousands) of dolphins (mainly striped dolphins) and whales are caught annually accidentally in drift nets set for swordfish by Italian fishery

9. Sri Lankan inshore gillnet fisheries have killed up to 42,000 dolphins and porpoises a year (mainly spinners) with large numbers of dolphins also killed in gillnet fisheries around the coasts of India

10. Unknown numbers of the rare Hector's dolphin are being caught accidentally in gillnets in New Zealand coastal waters

11. Up to 40,000 Dall's porpoises have been killed in the North Pacific by the squid and salmon drift net fishers of Japan

12. Well over 700 striped dolphins died as a result of a virus infection in the western Mediterranean between July and October 1990

13 Unknown numbers (but possibly in the low thousands) of harbour porpoises have been killed annually in the North Sea by the Danish 'wreck' fishery and others

14. Unknown numbers (but possibly in the thousands) of harbour porpoises are killed accidentally each year in coastal waters of S.W. Greenland, Canada and north-east United States by coastal gillnet fisheries

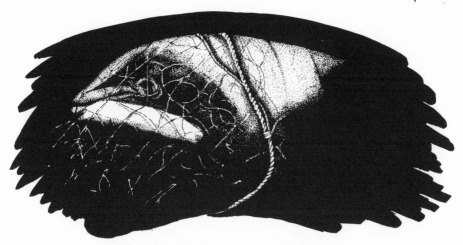

Hector's dolphin drowned in fishing net.

by other species such as mackerel and sprat, may be at least partly responsible for the comparative scarcity of cetaceans in all but the northern sector. Elsewhere, similar declines in fish stocks attributed to over-exploitation have included herring in western Norway and Japan, sardines in Japan and California, and capelin off eastern Canada and in the Barents Sea. Identifying the effects that such changes to fish populations have upon cetaceans is extremely difficult because of the complex interactions between predator and prey populations, and the many other factors such as climatic or oceanographic change, and pollution, that can affect both.

Accidental capture of dolphins in fishing gear, although known to have occurred since at least the Middle Ages, has become a large-scale threat to dolphin populations only in the last thirty years or so. The greatest damage known to have been caused to dolphin populations comes from the multinational tuna purse-seine fishery in the eastern tropical Pacific, where between 200,000 and 500,000 dolphins (mainly **spotted** and **spinner,** but also **common** and **Fraser's dolphins**) were killed annually during the 1960s and early 1970s. These deepwater dolphin species commonly associate with yellow-fin tuna and fishermen use the dolphins to help locate the shoals, but then encircle both tuna and dolphins in the nets. Altogether around 7 million dolphins have been estimated to die during this process in the last thirty years. Some of the populations declined considerably, the eastern Pacific stock of the **spinner dolphin** in particular being reduced by 80 per cent. In the 1980s, various measures were introduced to try to reduce the kill. These included adding a special panel of fine mesh (the 'Medina panel') furthest from the fishing vessels over which the dolphins were helped to escape. Nowadays the incidental take is lower, but still thought to number around 60,000-130,000 per year.

Incidental catches of dolphins are a worldwide problem, involving all sorts of fishing gear, but particularly gill-nets, either drifting or set in midwater or on the sea bottom. Virtually every species of cetacean has been caught by fishing gear at one time or another, although coastal species such as the **harbour** and **Burmeister's porpoises, vaquita** and **franciscana** seem to be worst affected. During a workshop organized by the International Whaling Commission in 1990 in La Jolla, California, 190 regional cetacean populations were identified as vulnerable to gill net fisheries. Incidental catches were found to be clearly unsustainable for 8 of these, and potentially unsustainable for a further 34. However, for 114 regional populations, the impact was unknown due to a complete lack of information. For many areas of the world, such as a large part of the coasts of south-east Asia, South America and Africa, and the high seas of all three major oceans where very large drift-net fisheries operate, incidental mortality could well be very high but merely unrecorded. Critical cases that have been identified include the **vaquita** in the Gulf of California and the **baiji** in the Yangtze River, both endangered species; the **Indo-Pacific hump-backed dolphin** in South Africa; the **striped dolphin** in the Mediterranean; the **harbour porpoise** in the eastern and western North Atlantic; and the **bottle-nosed dolphin** in South Africa.

We are still far away from finding practical solutions to the problem. In some cases, fishing practices have been modified or close seasons imposed and these have had positive effects. Scaring animals away or making the nets more detectable may also work in certain situations but neither is likely to be effective on the large scale that many of these fisheries operate. What *is* clear is that fishermen, scientists and fisheries managers are going to have to work closely together if the present annual take of several hundreds of thousands of animals is to be reduced.

Folklore and legend

Dolphins have been depicted in art and literature almost ever since the latter two have existed. The oldest drawing shows a man in a boat, close behind a seal and two porpoises. It was carved on a rock by Neolithic peoples 4,200 years ago, at Røddoy in northern Norway, and presumably the man is hunting the animals. Other drawings that have been found on Norwegian rocks portray various species of dolphin, apparently washed ashore.

Elsewhere, dolphins were depicted in ancient culture: drawings appear on frescoes in the Minoan temple of Knossos on the island of Crete 3,600 years ago, and dolphin (and whale) motifs are found on Greek vases, coins and even buildings. There is a mosaic floor on the site of the Basilica at Olous, Crete,

Dolphin mural at Knossos.

which depicts dolphins. In the British Museum in London, there is a beautiful Greek blown glass figure of a small cetacean from Boeotia dating to the first century BC. It may depict a Cuvier's beaked whale, a fairly common species in the Mediterranean even today. The Euphronius cup now in the Louvre, Paris, dating from 500 BC, is embellished with the scene of Theseus diving to the seabed surrounded by dolphins. Likewise, the Dionysus cup which dates from 540 BC shows the Greek god of wine Dionysus (Bacchus in Roman culture) in a vessel loaded with grapes and surrounded by dolphins. The wine god, Dionysus, turned men into dolphins when the crew of the ship on which he was travelling, disguised as a mortal human, decided to sell him into slavery on reaching land. The crew threw themselves overboard in terror when their plot was uncovered, and they were punished by having their ship overgrown with vines and the oars turned into serpents. On repenting, they were saved by Dionysus who transformed them into dolphins. This theme of transmutation between human and dolphin is widespread in ancient myths around the world.

Dolphins have been the subject of various Greek myths and legends, and the Maori people of New Zealand believed them to be messengers of the gods. The pre-Hellenic Cretans honoured dolphins as gods, and the ancient Greeks had a sanctuary in honour of the dolphin-god.

Perhaps the most famous of Greek legends is that of Arion, the lyric poet and musician, who, on returning to Corinth from Italy with riches that he had won at music competitions, was set upon by the crew of the boat in

which he was travelling. He begged to be allowed
one last favour, the chance to play a tune.
On being granted this, his music attracted a school of dolphins. When they
approached the boat, Arion leapt overboard and was carried to safety on the
back of one of the dolphins. This theme
recurs in many Mediterranean fables.
The Roman philosopher, Pliny the
Elder, recounts a tale of a boy living by
Lake Lucrino, Naples, who befriended
a dolphin which carried him across the
water each day to school. The boy died
while he was still young and his dolphin friend apparently pined to death
for his company. Pliny the Younger also

Greek coin: Arion being saved by a dolphin.

relates a story of a little boy at Hippo off the North African coast (now
Tunisia) being rescued from drowning and carried ashore on the back of a
dolphin (called 'Simo'). This was immortalized by the artist Raphael around
AD 1500, whose marble statue shows a fish-like dolphin (as they were thought
to be until the eighteenth century) but with apparently human teeth and
eyes. The statue may now be seen in the Hermitage Museum in Leningrad.

Whether tales such as those described above are based upon true experi-
ences is impossible to say, but they clearly show how from very early times,
humans have identified dolphins as showing altruistic behaviour, and have
developed a special relationship with them.

Whereas there are several passages in the Bible referring to dolphins (and
whales), and they were well integrated within Greek and Roman culture,
there is little evidence for them being exploited in the same way as they were
by the peoples of northern Europe. There are some reports of Mediterranean people catching dolphins, but for the most part it was thought a sin to
hurt or kill an animal that was so important in the ancient sagas and myths,
and which must have been a frequent companion to sailors at sea. Odysseus
proudly bore a crest with a dolphin upon it, and is depicted on Greek paintings at the mast of his boat with a dolphin in the background. Likewise,
dolphins always accompanied the god of the sea — the Roman Neptune, the
Greek Poseidon and the Finnish Wellamo.

Even 2,500 years ago, dolphins were known sufficiently well for their
appearance, anatomy and other aspects of their biology to be dscribed in
detail. The Greek philosopher Aristotle (384-322 BC) recorded dolphins as
having warm blood and lungs, giving birth to live young (as opposed to

laying eggs), and suckling their young just as other mammals do.

During the Middle Ages, the close scientific observation of people like Aristotle was cast aside, and Europe was dominated by myth and legend. A great number of imaginary animals are described in Konrad Gesner's famous text *Historia Animalium*, published in 1551. One of these depicts a horse with cloven hooves, a lion's tail, and a horn in the middle of the forehead — the unicorn. The horn of this animal bears a close resemblance to the long spiralled tusk of the **narwhal** of the high Arctic. Narwhal tusks were said to be endowed with miraculous properties and as a consequence an important trade in these tusks reached as far afield as southern Europe where they were ground into a powder with supposed medicinal properties (as an antidote against poisoning by arsenic and mercury, and to prevent bleeding). The tusk was highly prized, and specimens were presented to monarchs, used as bishops' croziers, and made into luxury items. In the early seventeenth century, the unicorn was introduced into the English royal coat of arms by King James I, reflecting its importance in west European culture.

Narwhals were probably hunted by Europeans for commercial purposes as early as the tenth century, soon after the Vikings had begun to establish permanent settlements in south-west Greenland, and ivory (and skins) were important export goods. The Norse Greenland Church took a special interest in procuring narwhal and walrus ivory, and settlers often paid their church tithes with ivory. The extensive trade between Greenland and Europe was

Narwhal and unicorn.

probably reduced by the late fourteenth century, and by the mid sixteenth century, no more than fifty tusks were known from outside hunting areas in Europe. The next phase of hunting probably began early in the seventeenth century as European whalers penetrated the Arctic waters of the Davis Strait and Baffin Bay.

In 1638, the Danish naturalist Ole Wurm identified the unicorn's tusk as that of the narwhal, and the reputation of apparent miraculous powers began to wane. Increasingly, they were consigned to museums and private collections although maintaining some value in the Orient, Russia and the Middle East. Even as late as the 1950s, powdered narwhal ivory was still being sold as a drug in Japan.

DOLPHINARIA

For many people, their first close view of a live dolphin will have been of a captive animal in a dolphinarium. The impact this has had upon public awareness and concern for dolphins is difficult to gauge but has probably been large. However, as people have become more aware of problems facing dolphins around the world, they also became increasingly concerned about the notion of keeping them in captivity in conditions that often left much to be desired.

Dolphins have been held for short periods in captivity since 1860, but it was not until 1938 that the first long-term display was set up when bottle-nosed dolphins were brought into captivity at St Augustine, Florida. Not until the 1950s did display facilities begin to be built in various parts of the United States, and the first one in Europe was opened to the public at Hardewijk in the Netherlands. Since then, over 4,600 small cetaceans have been captured alive for display (or research). The great majority of these were **bottle-nosed dolphins** (at least 2,700 animals taken between the 1860s and 1983, with minimum numbers of 1,595-1,635 from USA waters and 580 from Japanese waters).

In Europe, the first bottle-nosed dolphin recorded in captivity was one taken in UK waters in June 1883 and displayed at the Brighton Aquarium. Since 1962, up to 300 **bottle-nosed dolphins** and 8 **killer whales** have been imported into the UK for such purposes and there have been at least 30 dolphinaria. By 1990, this had declined to 13 animals and 4 dolphinaria and, following tighter legislative restrictions on minimum pool size and other aspects of husbandry to improve thei welfare, but which increased their running costs, all but one were forced to close. Dolphins from the last one, Flamingo Land in Yorkshire, were moved to a Swedish dolphinarium in the summer of 1993.

A review covering the United States, Canada, Europe, South Africa, Australasia, Japan, Indonesia and Hong Kong revealed 32 species amongst the more than 4,000 live captured mainly for display purposes. Next to bottle-

Risso's dolphin in dolphinarium.

nosed dolphins, the most common were **Pacific white-sided dolphins** (330), **short-finned pilot whales** (226), **spotted dolphins** (c. 150), **spinner dolphins** (c. 100), **white whales** (c. 100) and **killer whales**, (c. 110 — previously taken from the Pacific north-west but more recently mainly from Iceland).

The international trade in live specimens reached a peak in the early 1970s, but declined thereafter when restrictions imposed by the USA Marine Mammal Protection Act (1972) effectively cut off the main source of supply. Other factors included increased national and international legislation on wildlife trade in general (to reduce suffering and mortality), and the trend towards more permanent displays of social groups in which breeding (at least of bottle-nosed dolphins) could take place.

The conditions in which dolphins are kept vary tremendously between dolphinaria. Those facilities remaining in developed countries like the United States and Western Europe tend to be of a higher standard than those in south-east Asia. However, of the more than one hundred captive facilities in North America, differences in management and husbandry have led to great variation in survival rates for captive animals (average annual survival rate for bottle-nosed dolphins ranging from 1% to 98%). The overall average annual survival rate for dolphins was 93%, although only 61% of calves in their first year survived, this increased to 97% subsequently. Although this latter figure does not differ significantly from 95% annual survival for adult bottle-nosed dolphins in the wild, the survival rate of calves (up to one year) in the wild appears to be much higher, at somewhere between 73 and 87 per cent.

The keeping of dolphins in captivity remains a highly controversial subject. On the one hand, people argue that they provide large numbers of people, particularly children, with opportunities for close direct contact with dolphins in a way that is not possible through television, cinema, books and magazines. They also allow scientists to carry out close-up studies in controlled conditions in a way that would not be possible in the wild. On the other hand, captive dolphins generally suffer sensory deprivation and stress causing various psychological disorders such as stereotyped behaviour, aggression and self-inflicted injury. Except under the best conditions of husbandry, they may also suffer actual mortality both during capture and transport, and particularly during the initial stages of captivity.

Pollution

In the last fifty years, many parts of the world have witnessed a substantial increase in industrialization which has brought with it major pollution problems particularly in semi-enclosed waters such as the Baltic and North Seas, Mediterranean and Black Seas, and the Gulfs of Mexico and St Lawrence.

One of the earliest compounds recognized to cause marine pollution was oil, after the widespread introduction of oil-burning engines for shipping in the early part of this century. Although large oil spills such as the *Torrey Canyon*, *Amoco Cadiz*, *Exxon Valdez* and *Braer* are the ones that hit the headlines, most oil enters the marine environment through the routine cleaning out of ships' fuel tanks. Of the estimated 3.2 million tonnes of oil that enter the sea annually, nearly 45 per cent is from marine transportation, including spills. Marine birds are the most conspicuous casualties, but deaths associated with oil have been reported for seals, sea otters, dugongs and cetaceans. Our knowledge of the effects of oil contamination upon dolphins remains very poor. Observations of **bottle-nosed dolphins** in the vicinity of an oil slick in the Gulf of Mexico showed that whereas they appeared to recognize and avoid the presence of heavily weathered oil which had formed a 'mousse', they travelled straight through light oil sheens on the surface. Their presence in the middle of light surface oil exposes them to highly volatile toxic fumes which may cause inflammation of mucous membranes, lung congestion and pneumonia. Much probably depends on the duration of exposure; inhaled volatile hydrocarbons are certain to accumulate in the blood and tissues, where they may induce liver damage and neurological disorders.

Two classes of pollutants affecting dolphins give particular cause for concern: these are synthetic organic compounds (organochlorine pesticides such as DDT, mirex, endrin, and dieldrin, generally referred to as 'chlorinated hydrocarbons'); industrial organo-chlorines such as polychlorinated biphenyls (PCBs); and organometals such as tributyl tin (TBT)) and heavy metals (such as mercury, lead, cadmium and zinc). These substances reach the sea through direct or indirect industrial discharges, rivers, storm and irrigation run-off from land, ocean dumping and atmospheric deposition. They are widely distributed in the oceans, persistent, and, being carried by wind and water, may be found from the poles to the tropics.

Most animals have a limited ability to break down these compounds, which if lipid-soluble (as is the case with organic compounds and most metals), accumulate as the animal gets older in fatty tissues such as blubber, but otherwise (as in mercury, cadmium and other metals) enter organs such as the liver, kidneys or brain. Although quantities of these pollutants in the sea may be minute, they are concentrated in the bodies of marine plankton which are then ingested by fish and squid which in turn fall prey to larger predators such as marine birds and mammals. The higher up the food chain an animal is, the greater will be the concentration of pollutants in its body: a process referred to as bioaccumulation. Dolphins are amongst those animal groups at the very top of the marine food chain, and so are likely to have the highest levels of these pollutants.

Several of the trace metals (including zinc and mercury) occur naturally in the environment, and, at least in small quantities, appear to be beneficial to animals, being important in certain enzyme reactions. However, above certain levels they can become toxic. Three metals (mercury, lead and cadmium) are of greatest concern.

Mercury affects a wide range of organs, particularly the brain, nervous system and kidneys, and it may reduce resistance to disease. Most mercury in the sea occurs in the organic form (methyl mercury) which is particularly toxic, but marine mammals seem to have the ability to store mercury in the liver in a relatively inert inorganic form, and the mercury usually occurs with another metal, selenium, which is known to reduce its toxic effect. Some regions appear to be hot spots for mercury contamination. In the UK, for example, grey seals in the Irish Sea have been found with mercury levels up to 860 parts per million (generally abbreviated to 'ppm'); by comparison, **harbour porpoises** had levels up to 150 ppm, a **long-finned pilot whale** had 370 ppm, and an **Atlantic white-sided dolphin** 44 ppm. The highest level for any cetacean is 1,544 ppm in a **striped dolphin** from the Mediterranean coast of France, although this was believed to derive from local natural deposits. As yet we do not know if any of these levels is harmful to marine mammals.

In most parts of the world, lead enters the marine ecosystem mainly from car exhaust emissions. In animals, it is absorbed through the gut and respiratory tract and can cause severe encephalopathy which in turn may lead to brain damage. Concentrations in marine mammals tend to be low (generally less than 1 ppm). In the UK, the highest level was 7 ppm in a grey seal from the Irish Sea, and the highest values in a dolphin were 3.8 ppm in a **white-beaked dolphin** and 4.3 ppm in a **harbour porpoise**, also from the Irish Sea. Again, there is no evidence that these levels had harmed the animals which were examined.

Cadmium is often associated with zinc and lead, and can be highly toxic. Although usually inhaled where it can cause severe lung damage, in marine mammals it is most likely to be ingested from prey such as shellfish which can accumulate high concentrations. In the UK, the highest levels in a dolphin were 8.4 and 11 ppm in two **striped dolphins** (probably reflecting their diet) stranded in West Wales. Elsewhere, maximum values recorded are all low: 11 ppm in a **striped dolphin** in Japan, 21

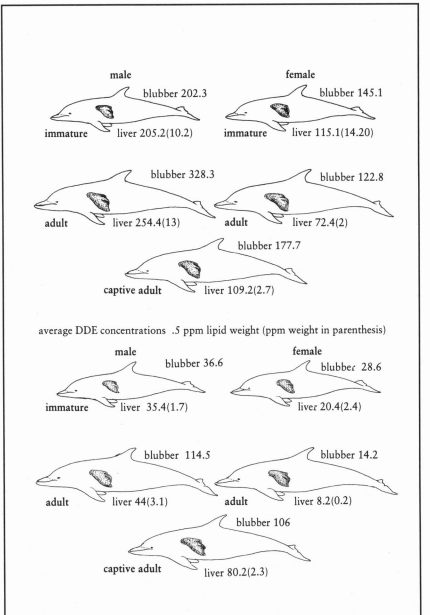

male
blubber 202.3
immature liver 205.2(10.2)

female
blubber 145.1
immature liver 115.1(14.20)

blubber 328.3
adult liver 254.4(13)

blubber 122.8
adult liver 72.4(2)

blubber 177.7
captive adult liver 109.2(2.7)

average DDE concentrations .5 ppm lipid weight (ppm weight in parenthesis)

male
blubber 36.6
immature liver 35.4(1.7)

female
blubber 28.6
liver 20.4(2.4)

blubber 114.5
adult liver 44(3.1)

blubber 14.2
adult liver 8.2(0.2)

blubber 106
captive adult liver 80.2(2.3)

Relative pollutant burdens in dolphin livers.

ppm in **Dall's porpoise** in the north-west Pacific, 42 ppm in a dolphins and man ommon dolphin in France, and 43 ppm in a **striped dolphin** in Italy.

Organochlorines have been in widespread use in agriculture and industry since the 1920s. Although a number of compounds are difficult to detect and their biological effects are unknown, there are some that we know are particularly dangerous. These are a group of insecticides that includes DDT, mirex and dieldrin, and the PCBs used particularly as hydraulic fluid in electrical transformers and as fire retardants. Production of these organochlorines reached a peak during the 1960s when their toxicity was first recognized, but declined thereafter at least in Western Europe and North America, following tight controls. However, their manufacture and discharge has continued in other parts of the world. In the case of PCBs, around 70 per centof the 1.5 million tonnes produced since 1929 is still in use. Even if use of these chemicals ceased immediately, because of their persistence, they will remain in the environment for a long time to come.

Because of the similarity of some organochlorines to biological molecules, their presence in an animal's blood induces the activity of particular enzymes to break them down. In so doing, some of the animal's steroid hormones are also broken down, leading to a hormonal imbalance which can impair reproduction. Furthermore, some PCB molecules have a strong tendency to combine with a blood chemical called transthyretin which is involved in the transport of vitamin A and thyroid hormones to which it is bound. When PCBs do this, large quantities of the thyroid hormone and vitamin A remain in circulation and become excreted by the kidneys, and this may leave them more vulnerable to infection. Evidence that such biological effects may occur in marine mammals comes primarily from experimental studies in Holland upon seals fed a diet of contaminated fish which were less likely to become pregnant and had lower thyroid hormone and vitamin A levels than those fed on uncontaminated fish. Otherwise, a study of Dall's porpoise in Japan showed a correlation between increasing PCB and DDT concentrations in blubber and decreasing concentrations of a male sex hormone (testosterone), and a study of striped dolphins, also in Japanese waters, indicated abnormalities in lipid metabolism in individuals with high PCB and DDT burdens.

In 1988, some 17,000 common seals died from an outbreak of the morbillivirus called phocine distemper virus, in the North Sea. The mortality was greatest in the southernmost part where animals also have relatively high organochlorine levels. A high proportion of dead seals examined in Germany had abnormalities of the thyroid gland and some had much higher organochlorine levels than survivors sampled six months later. It was therefore speculated that pollutants might have suppressed the immune system, making them more vulnerable to disease. However, those effects could also have been caused directly by the virus infection.

In 1990, at least 750 striped dolphins in the Mediterranean died from an epidemic caused by a closely related morbillivirus. They too had very high levels of PCBs (up to 2,965 ppm in blubber), but with relatively large quantities also in their livers suggesting that the PCBs had been mobilized from fat reserves in the blubber. The average PCB levels in the blubber of dead animals from the epidemic was 886 ppm, three times as high as the average value (309 ppm) for apparently healthy animals biopsied in the region in previous years. When these values are recalculated in terms of body loads, the casualties of the epidemic still had PCB levels twice as high as those previously sampled. This suggests that the high levels were not due solely to the nutritional condition of the dolphins (i.e. to the dolphins being starved and so mobilizing the PCBs from the blubber into the liver). As to whether the virus infection or PCB contamination caused the mass die-off, we shall never know, but this does serve to highlight the difficulty in teasing apart various factors which can closely interact with each other.

Where analyses of the contaminant levels of organochlorines have been carried out upon marine mammals, concentrations have tended to be highest in those regions (for example Mediterranean, Irish Sea, Gulf of St Lawrence) known to be most polluted. In some of these areas, contaminant levels in marine mammals are so high that they would necessitate a government health warning if anyone had thought of eating them! The small, and seriously declining population of white whales in the St Lawrence estuary and Gulf of St Lawrence include some of the most contaminated individuals ever recorded, with PCB levels as high as 1,725 ppm. Such contamination is blamed for the poor reproduction and high rate of disease observed in this regional population.

Dolphins often seem to have higher levels than seals from the same region and this may support other evidence that they are less able to break down PCBs than seals. For this very reason, dolphins might also be less badly affected since they should not produce as many of the harmful metabolites. Furthermore, not only may variations in PCB levels in blubber not necessarily reflect their actual harm to the animal, but our analytical measurements may be inappropriate. Of the 209 known individual PCB constituents (referred to as 'congeners') occurring in commercial mixtures, only about one hundred occur in forms that may enter the marine environment, and the subset which are believed to be most toxic (referred to as 'coplanar PCBs') make up only 1per cent of this mixture. At present there is no reliable and accurate method to measure concentrations of the toxic coplanars or the various breakdown products of PCBs, and instead we have to assume that their concentrations are reflected in those of the overall mixture or, in more recently refined analyses, the more easily measured individual congeners.

A recent study in the UK found no difference in PCB levels between porpoises that had died of disease or starvation and those suffering trauma or entanglement in fishing gear. On the other hand, there have been a few cases of dolphin strandings in the UK where high contaminant levels are suspected of having caused their deaths. In June 1988, a dead 9-month-old **bottlenosed dolphin** was found floating a mile offshore in Cardigan Bay, West Wales, with 290 ppm PCBs and 150 ppm DDT in its blubber. Cause of death was diagnosed as hepatitis although the possibility that this was due to a virus could not be excluded. These very high levels of organochlorine contamination reflect an important feature of these chemicals. Studies of bottlenosed dolphin in eastern North America and South Africa (and of other species like the harbour porpoise and white whale) have emphasized how concentrations build up as individuals grow older but with the distinction that this generally applies only to males; the contaminant burden of females tends to decline the older she is, due to the passing on of her contaminants to the calf first through the placenta and later in her milk.

Although we remain unclear about the biological effects of organochlorines and heavy metals upon dolphins, their widespread and persistent presence in the marine environment can do no good. In 1990, the national governments of European countries bordering the North Sea agreed to phase out and destroy all identifiable PCBs (and a number of other toxic chemicals) in use by 1999. This precautionary step is definitely to be welcomed, but whether it can be carried out effectively, and applied also to other regions where such organochlorines continue to be produced/used, remains very uncertain.

FRIENDLY DOLPHINS

One feature of dolphins that excites the human imagination perhaps more than any other is the friendliness that individuals show us on occasions. Altogether, at least ten species have been recorded socializing with humans. Mostly they are species that occur in coastal waters, and by far the most frequently recorded is the **bottle-nosed dolphin.**

For most people, the sociability of wild dolphins is exhibited by simple bow-riding of the vessel in which they are travelling. But on some occasions, individual dolphins befriend humans, allowing or even encouraging physical contact, and discriminating between people even when clad in different guises such as wetsuit or out of the water in dry clothes. This kind of sociability seems to start with extreme inquisitiveness on the part of the dolphin. The initial contact may be an animal swimming close to boats that are regularly in the area. This may then progress to direct approaches to human swimmers and divers. As familiarity increases, and particularly if the humans show encouragement, closer and more prolonged contact may then occur. These initial stages can span a protracted period. For example, 'Percy', a male bottle-nosed dolphin, was first seen off Portreath, Cornwall, in January 1981. It started following the local lobster and crab fishing boat, visiting each buoyed trap as it was being inspected, but did not permit any body contact with swimmers until two years later when it became physically quite friendly. 'Donald', another male bottle-nosed dolphin, first seen off the west coast of England in April 1972, approached people at a much earlier stage of contact, although actual handling and touch-

Divers often form close relationships with dolphins.

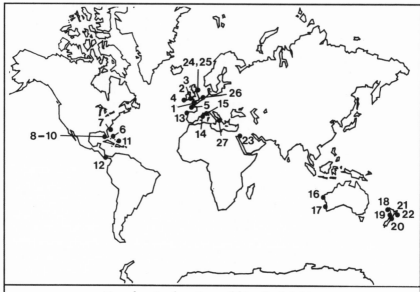

Map showing locations of friendly dolphins.

1. 'Percy': male bottle-nosed dolphin at Portreath, Cornwall, 1981-4

2. 'Donald' ('Beaky'): male bottle-nosed dolphin at Isle of Man, West Wales and S.W. England, 1972-8

3. 'Simo': male bottle-nosed dolphin at Solva, West Wales, 1984-6

4. 'Funghi' ('Dorad'): male bottle-nosed dolphin at Dingle, Co. Kerry, 1987-present

5. 'Jean-Louis': female bottle-nosed dolphin near Cap du Roz, Brittany, France, 1979-87

6. 'Sandy': spinner dolphin at San Salvador, Bahamas, 1976-8 + bottle-nosed dolphin off Harbor Island, Bahamas, 1987

7. 'Carolina Snowball': female bottle-nosed dolphin, S. Carolina to Georgia, 1950s

8. 'Dolly': female bottle-nosed dolphin at Key West, Florida, 1960s

9. 'Georgy Girl': female bottle-nosed dolphin (later joined by male) in Florida, 1960s

10. 'Nudgy': male bottle-nosed dolphin at Phillips Inlet, Florida, 1981

11. Bottle-nosed dolphin at Groce Bay, Turks and Caicos Islands, 1990

12. Bottle-nosed dolphin at Chira, Costa Rica, 1983

13. 'Nina': female bottle-nosed dolphin at La Coruna, Spain, 1972

14. Bottle-nosed dolphin at Cape Creus, north of Barcelona, Spain, 1986-7

15. 'Fanny': female bottle-nosed dolphin at Pointe de Caro, near Marseilles, France, 1987

ing did not occur for several months. In 1972, 'Nina', a female bottle-nosed dolphin off La Coruna, Spain, first approached a clam diver, and then sought body contact within only a few weeks, and Wade Doak reports several encounters with bottle-nosed and common dolphins where they would spontaneously accompany his Polynesian cameraman and would play with swimmers from his boat. On the other hand, another famous dolphin, a female bottle-nosed named 'Jean-Louis', spent over seven years from September 1979 off Pointe du Raz, Brittany, France in close proximity to humans, chasing and playing 'tricks' on swimmers and divers but never actually allowing body contact. This highlights the individual variability in response to humans that dolphins can show.

Ancient legends of children riding on the backs of dolphins were translated into reality for the people of Hokianga Harbour (Opononi, New Zealand) in the mid-1950s when a female bottle-nosed dolphin called 'Opo' allowed children to mount her and ride astride her back. This dolphin first started out as an inquisitive stray which would follow boats in the neighbourhood but became highly social after an excursion into the beach area was greeted enthusiastically by local children and holidaymakers attempting to make physical contact.

Although 'friendly' dolphins have tended to be solitary individuals, close ob-

16. Group of more than 7 bottle-nosed dolphins, Monkey Mia, Shark Bay (W. Australia) more than 20 years to present

17. Bottle-nosed dolphins at Ilumbana Bay 1989

18. '**Opo**': female bottle-nose dolphin at Opononi near Hokianga, 1955

19. '**Tammy**': male dusky dolphin at Taranaki Estuary, North Island, 1984

20. '**Pelorus Jack**': male Risso's dolphin in Cook Strait, 1888-c.1912

21. '**Tammy**': male dusky dolphin at Tamaki estuary, New Zealand

22. '**Horace**': male bottle-nosed dolphin at Napier, North Island, 1978

23. '**Debbie**': male bottle-nosed dolphin at Eilat, Red Sea, 1970s

24. '**Charlie**': female bottle-nosed dolphin, Fife, Scotland to Northumberland, England, c.1962-7

25. '**Freddie**' ('**Dougal**'): male bottle-nosed dolphin at Amble, Northumberland, 1986-present

26. Male bottle-nosed dolphin, Holland, 1990-present

27. Female bottle-nosed dolphin at Bay of Kotor, Yugoslavia, 1987-8

servation supplemented with photographs of 'Percy' in Cornwall, showed that over an extended period, tooth-rake scars appeared, presumably made by other dolphins, and suggesting that social contact with other dolphins took place periodically when he temporarily disappeared from his usual haunts. The stimulus for apparently seeking human contact is not clear. It has been speculated that the friendly individuals are 'outcasts' from dolphin society, but there is no evidence for them being misfits, and their behaviour parallels that observed in dolphins within groups and in other situations (including in captivity). More likely, some are victims of circumstance, either orphans or temporary strays which may then become 'incorporated' into human groups. Friendly individuals may be of either sex and any age, although they tend to be either young or old individuals, both age groups at which movement between schools is more likely to occur.

There are a few instances where friendly dolphins are not alone, either approaching humans in small groups, or breaking away from the group for temporary but regular association with humans. At Monkey Mia in Shark Bay, Western Australia, several bottle-nosed dolphins have become habituated to humans since the late 1960s. At least ten individuals (recognized by unique markings) regularly come inshore to water less than one metre deep to get close to holidaymakers who hand-feed them fish. The fish (which can be dead and half-frozen) are accepted though not always eaten, sometimes instead being used as playthings and then dropped. Elsewhere, solitary dolphins usually do not accept fish although they will play with them. The hand-feeding of some of the Monkey Mia dolphins has not only habituated them to humans but also provided excellent opportunities for detailed scientific observation on the behaviour of a free-living group of dolphins.

'Friendly' dolphins can be less than gentle. There have been many instances of mischievous behaviour where the dolphin has pushed swimmers and even surfers out to sea, or actively prevented them from swimming ashore, or pinned divers to the seabed. Sometimes the dolphin can show unexpected bouts of aggression, butting swimmers in the chest, overturning boats or smashing up surfboards as people rode into shore. Between 1988 and 1992, a male bottle-nosed dolphin called Freddie befriended humans at the mouth of the River Coquet at Amble in Northumberland, Eastern England. It would sometimes show aggression towards divers as well as behaviour that, although appearing overtly sexual (see page 36), may have had more to do with establishing dominance. After being injured by the propellor of a boat, it wandered up and down along the coast for a while before disappearing altogether in March 1992.

Habitat degradation and disturbance

In addition to the toxic chemicals with which we pollute our seas, and human waste such as sewage with its cocktail of potentially harmful diseases, dolphin habitats face further pressures from habitat degradation. The species most affected are those with restricted distributions, particularly where they are tied to rivers or coastal areas where their habitat requirements prevent them from escaping human activities. In particular, these are members of the porpoise family and the river dolphins.

River dolphins are affected by modifications to the flow of rivers by the construction of barrages for hydroelectric development. The **Ganges susu**, for example, continues to decline rapidly in the rivers of Nepal, where there may be only about 40 remaining, and further high dams are planned for the region. Elsewhere in India and in Pakistan, the construction of dams and barrages has fragmented populations of **Ganges** and **Indus susus**, causing local extinctions perhaps because of disruption of their food supplies. Damming and other developments also threaten **boto** populations in Brazil, and have seriously affected **white whale** populations in the outer St Lawrence estuary by closing important feeding grounds, following hydroelectric developments on the Manicougan River. Coastal development is also thought to threaten **franciscana** populations along the coasts of Brazil and Venezuela, and the **vaquita** in the upper reaches of the Gulf of California.

Harrassment by increased vessel traffic is another new problem facing coastal dolphins. Sometimes the effects are obvious, as in the case of animals damaged by collisions with boats and their propellors. Several **baiji**, for example, are thought to die annually in collisions with vessels on the Yangtze river, where it has become the most endangered of all cetacean species.

In most cases, however, the effects of disturbance are much more difficult

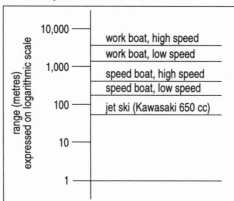

Ranges of detectability of various seagoing craft.

to determine. Concern has been expressed over disturbance by whale-watchers to regular concentrations of **white whales** in Bristol Bay, Alaska and the St Lawrence estuary, Canada, and to larger species like **gray whales** and **hump-backs** in southern California, Mexico, Hawaii and Alaska. So far, there have been few reports of dolphins being affected detrimentally by people watching them, although the pursuit of **bottle-nosed dolphins** by speedboats in the UK has caused local concern.

Many sea areas have seen a large increase in marine traffic, which in some places has been estimated to lead to a rise in ambient noise levels of about 10 dB. Most of these sounds, however, are predominantly in the frequency range 10-100 Hz with very little above 1 kHz. The greatest hearing sensitivity of dolphins and porpoises is 1-150 kHz and so should not be greatly affected by such vessels, although dolphin hearing does extend down to about 20 Hz.

Speedboats, particularly when there is cavitation of the propellor, generate sound in the 100 Hz to 20 kHz band range, so fall within the dolphin's range. Above 2 kHz, cavitation is the most significant source of noise. At the higher frequencies, sounds are attenuated rapidly in shallow water and will only be heard short distances away. A recent study carried out by the author and colleagues in Cardigan Bay, West Wales indicated that when the sea gets choppy (measured by a rating of at least 3 on the Beaufort scale) a 650 cc outboard jetski would be detectable to a dolphin up to 450 m away, a small 6 hp outboard inflatable at about 1 km, a rigid hull 90 hp outboard speedboat at 0.8 (low)- 1.8 km (high speed), and a 50-foot 240 hp inboard fishing boat at 1.1 (low)-3.1 km (high speed). During this study, bottle-nosed dolphins responded with avoiding action to speedboats, with individuals making significantly longer dives and moving away from the sound source.

In the last twenty years, oil exploration involving seismic surveys has occurred in cold temperate and Arctic regions of Europe and North America. The sounds produced by airgun arrays during seismic surveys are mainly between 8 and 200 Hz (particularly below 80 Hz), and may be transmitted great distances. Source levels now are around 200 decibels (at 1 metre distance). Studies of the effects of seismic sound upon large whales have generally shown responses when received levels are more than 160-170 dB, which theoretically would be at distances of 100 metres (in the 1970s and early 1980s when louder equipment was used, such sound levels would extend to 4-7.5 km).

When received levels fall to about 120 dB (i.e. at a theoretical distance of 10 km), sounds from other vessels are more likely to cause an adverse reaction. It should be noted, however, that these values may be modified by a variety of factors — sea conditions, bottom topography, water depth, position of the animal in the water column, etc. Nevertheless, in general, we may conclude that as with large vessels, sounds made by seismic surveys are more likely to affect mysticete whales, whose hearing range are primarily between 12 and 30 Hz, than dolphins.

Dolphin Future

Over the last 100,000 years, *Homo sapiens* and members of the order *Cetacea* have shared this planet: partners in evolution, one coming to dominate the terrestrial environment and the other the sea. In the most recent 4,000 years, as humans have extended their domain to encompass the sea, a relationship has been built up with dolphins and whales that has moved back and forth between idolatry and exploitation.

Our present century has seen a human population explosion, and accelerating demands on the environment for food and other resources as countries around the world become ever more industrialized. To date, the main threat to the great whales has been from overhunting. Whaling in the last hundred years has greatly reduced populations of most species, as modern exploitation, usually for commercial purposes, has seriously overshot sustainable levels. An increasing awareness of, and concern for, the plight of the whales has led to hunting regulations which in several cases have amounted to complete bans. For the time being, the large whales are reasonably protected from direct killing. Dolphins, on the other hand, receive relatively little protection around the world.

Dolphins are hunted by humans mainly for local subsistence or because they are perceived as a threat to fishing activities, rather than for commercial reasons. However, in both cases they may lead to the development of some trade, which in turn is most likely to result in over-exploitation (see pages 83-5). Sometimes, accidental captures in fishing nets can be transformed into a directed fishery, as has happened for example in Peru. Following the collapse of local stocks of anchoveta, many fishermen have shifted to using gillnets to hunt dolphins, particularly **dusky dolphins**, with annual catches now exceeding 10,000 in some years.

Nowadays, by far the largest takes of cetaceans are by-catches in fishing gear. We have little idea of the true extent of the kill, but almost certainly it numbers several hundreds of thousands every year. Even where by-catches are small, they may seriously endanger local populations or species of low population size, as is feared for the **baiji** and **vaquita**.

The incidental mortality of dolphins caused by capture in fishing gear in many cases is visible and can be monitored (even if at present such monitoring rarely takes place). The effects upon dolphin survival and reproduction of competition with fisheries for food, of chemical pollution, sound disturbance and other forms of habitat degradation are generally much more difficult to determine. Yet it is habitat modification that has probably caused more animal extinctions than any other human pressure. Despite all that man has thrown against them, no cetacean species has to our knowledge

PREVIOUS PAGE: Hector's dolphin.

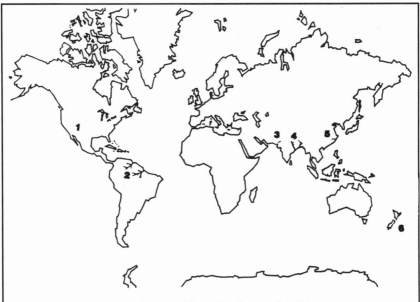

Distribution of vulnerable and endangered dolphin species.

1. Vaquita: population in low hundreds in northern end of Gulf of California

2. Boro: populations in the main rivers of the Orinoco and Amazon basins of unknown size but facing serious threats throughout its range

3. Indus river dolphin: population in low hundreds, in river Indus in Pakistan

4. Ganges river dolphin: population size unknown but declining rapidly in rivers Ganges and Brahmaputra

5. Baisi: population around 300 individuals in Changjiang (Yangtze river)

6. Hector's dolphin: population estimated to number in low thousands; confined to coastal waters of New Zealand (mainly off South Island) and facing threats from entanglement in fishing nets gone extinct in historic times (though some local populations have been wiped out). However, two river dolphins (the **baiji** and **Indus susu**) and the coastal porpoise, the **vaquita**, are in danger of extinction, with total populations numbering in the low hundreds. The river dolphins and coastal porpoises with their restricted habitat preferences, often close to man, are particularly vulnerable to habitat modification, and could be the first cetacean candidates for extinction.

Even when a serious threat can be identified, it is often hard to remove the cause in a world of so many conflicting interests. For scientists and conservationists to work closely with other groups to achieve a joint solution of these many problems must be *the* major challenge of the 21st century.

Dead vaquita on Californian beach.

Modern research

Until around tweny-five years ago, virtually all our knowledge about dolphins came either from dead animals washed ashore or killed in direct hunts, or from those held in captivity for display and research purposes. Living often far from land and spending about ninety-five per cent of their lives below the water surface, dolphins (and their whale cousins) have remained amongst the least known of mammal groups. Some species have scarcely ever been seen alive, and of the forty-five species covered by this volume, only half a dozen have been studied in any detail. Most of those are ones with coastal populations, such as the **bottle-nosed dolphin, harbour porpoise** and **killer whale**, which scientists can study without venturing too far from their terrestrial domains.

In the early days of modern cetology, studies of living dolphins were carried out mainly in captive situations, and particularly upon one species, the **bottle-nosed dolphin,** which appeared more capable of adapting to those restrictive conditions than most other dolphins or larger whales. Some of those studies were motivated by selfish needs. Research on aspects of health and nutrition of dolphins, including disease agents, blood chemistry and general physiology, was often related to commercial needs to maintain animals in captivity and encourage them to reproduce. The United States Navy used dolphins for planting and retrieving explosives and to guard or locate military equipment. For those purposes, research was undertaken on sensory discrimination and learning abilities of dolphins.

For various aspects of cetacean biology, however, research on captive animals has provided the primary, if not only, source of knowledge. The opportunity to closely watch dolphins of known sex, age, reproductive and social status for extended periods has enabled us to learn much about their individual and social behaviour such as feeding, courtship, play, parental care, and aggression. Likewise, the controlled conditions of a tank have allowed experiments on the physiology and mechanics of swimming and diving, vision, echolocation and communication, estimates of food intake and determination of energy budgets.

The taxonomy of dolphins and basic information about their biology has traditionally derived from examination of dead animals. In a number of countries, extensive schemes are in place to monitor strandings. Some of these have been operating for many years: the strandings scheme in Britain run by the London Natural History Museum was set up, for example, in 1913. When a dolphin dies and is washed ashore, the cetacean scientist takes various external body measurements (for example body length and, if possible, weight), records its sex and if female, looks for evidence that it is pregnant or lactating, and removes a tooth for later sectioning and microscopic examination to determine its age from the number of growth layers laid down.

If the animal is fresh and can be transported, it is usually removed to a laboratory where a more detailed examination occurs that may take several hours. The thickness of the blubber may be measured, and tissue and organ samples (particularly blubber, muscle, liver, and kidney) taken and frozen for chemical analysis to provide information on the amount of heavy metals and organochlorines that have accumulated in them. Samples of blood, skin, or organs such as liver are frozen or placed in a preservative for genetic studies. Particularly with recent developments in DNA techniques, such analyses have been used to determine sex, paternity and genetic relationships between social groups, populations and species. Examination of the sexual organs not only provides information on the reproductive status of the animal but also can reveal much about its reproductive history such as the number of calves borne by a female. From a sample of individuals it is then possible to calculate various important population parameters such as average age of sexual maturity, mating and calving seasons, gestation and lactation periods and reproductive rates.

Other internal examinations provide information on the health status and possible cause of death — parasite burdens, and presence of bacterial or viral agents of disease. If the animal fed recently before death, its stomach contents may still contain the hard parts of fish (otoliths) and squid (beaks) which can often be identified to species and thus provide valuable information on diet.

One of the greatest developments in cetacean research in the last two decades has been the study of live cetaceans at sea. During the 1970s, this took the form of counts of whales and dolphins from land or by boat and aircraft surveys, whereas in the past numbers were calculated from examination of dead animals. Since those days, methods have become ever more refined, to try to take account of the proportion of animals missed along a cruise track and the varying distances at which particular species are detected under different conditions of viewing height, sea state, etc (at low elevations and high sea states, individuals of most species will only be seen close to the vessel, the rest being hidden behind waves). Such problems as these are still far from being entirely overcome, not least because dolphins are only poorly detected by visual means; also because calculations of abundance can be unreliable in areas where a species is rare because the estimates are of necessity based on small sample sizes. In some cases, acoustic surveys have been carried out involving recording with hydrophones the presence of dolphins by the sounds they make. However, these also have their limitations: dolphins may be silent and go undetected (this seems to be more of a problem for baleen whales than for dolphins), estimating detectability distances is not always easy, and determining numbers of individuals within groups is a major problem.

The above methods provide estimates of the numbers of animals in a prescribed area; by extrapolation, so long as the entire area has been sampled in a representative manner, an estimate of the population size can be made. Alternatively, if an index of abundance is sufficient for comparison between areas or from one time period to another, the numbers of a particular species detected per unit effort (for example by number of kilometres travelled, or, from a fixed land-based site, the number of minutes or hours watched) can be calculated.

Another way of establishing a population estimate is referred to as the 'mark-recapture method', where a sample of a given population is marked in some way and then compared with the proportion of marked animals found in a subsequent sample (this sample is no longer recaptured but is usually photographed). In the past this was used in the whaling industry by firing 'Discovery' tags into a sample of whales and recovering a proportion later when subsequently captured by the whalers. Nowadays, the 'mark-

Bottle-nosed dolphin ID features.

recapture' technique uses photographs of natural markings such as scars, pigmentation patterns, and nicks in the dorsal fin on live animals to recognize individuals — a technique referred to as photo-ID. This has the advantage that a population can be 'marked' and many times 'recaptured' (by photography) without need to actually capture or harm animals.

Photo-ID has revolutionized our knowledge of the lives of individual animals at sea. It has provided information on many important biological parameters including home ranges, associations between individuals, age and sex differences in behaviour, reproductive rates and lifespans. Some species (such as **bottle-nosed dolphin** and **killer whale**) appear to be better marked and so more amenable to this type of study than others (such as the porpoises). However, as new species are investigated in detail, more and more are showing individual differences in markings for a proportion of the population, and it may be that by close observation the technique can be applied to most cetacean species.

Since the 1960s, another technique, called radio telemetry, has been used widely upon a variety of animal species to determine individual movements and home ranges, and various aspects of behaviour and physiology. A transmitter sending pulsed radio signals, usually in the frequency range 30-401 MHz, is attached in some way to the animal. The signal is then detected by one or more remote receivers. In the case of marine animals like dolphins, these may be on land, boats, aircraft or, more recently, on satellites. Information from the signal normally includes the position of the animal (by triangulation from different receiving positions), but may also give details of its physiology and behaviour (such as activity, swimming patterns, heart rate) as well as various environmental conditions (for example, water temperature and pressure, depth of dive).

Radio transmitters have become much smaller in the last fifteen years, and in cetaceans no longer necessarily require attachment by capture of the animal. Using a modified gun, a transmitter with radio antenna can be fired into the blubber of the animal although after a time the tissue will reject it, and it will fall off. Satellite-linked telemetry has been the most recent innovation. Since satellites continually scan the entire surface of the earth, there is no need to spend money and time on following the animal by boat or aircraft. Although on cetaceans it was first applied to the large whales such as **gray** and **humpback**, it has now been used on a number of smaller species such as **white whale** and **bottle-nosed dolphin**.

Methods of collecting information about the lives of cetaceans without need to capture or harm them continue to develop. Scientists may now follow animals and scoop up their faeces for analyses of diet and reproductive state; they may fire an arrow from a crossbow to take tiny samples of skin for genetic analysis and sexing; they spend comparatively long periods of time underwater amongst dolphins, either scuba diving or in a submersible; and we are now seeing remote control techniques using fibre optics for filming underwater and collecting environmental information starting to be used.

As human interest and concern for dolphins continues to grow, increasing numbers of people want to have the opportunity to see them at close quarters. When 'friendly' dolphins make at least temporary contact with humans, the appetite to interact with them is almost unquenchable. In the last few years, more than 100,000 people a year have visited Monkey Mia in Western Australia to see the friendly local **bottle-nosed dolphins.** Total revenues to the region from such visitors is estimated at £10.15 million per annum. In Europe, around 150,000 people in a year (1991) visited Dingle in

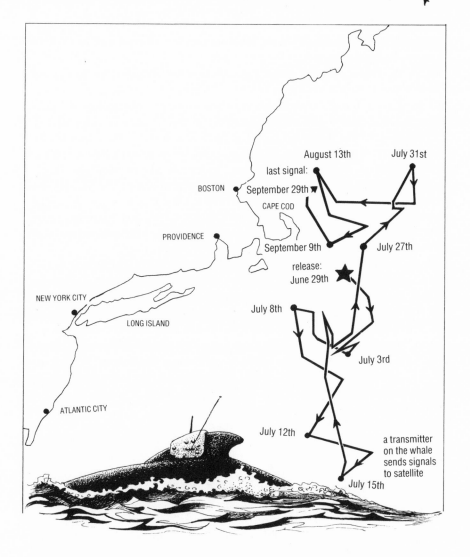

From July when it was released, until October when the battery became exhausted, the movements of 'Tag', the pilot whale, were tracked, as revealed by signals from his satellite transmitter.

Western Ireland to see the local bottle-nosed dolphin variously called 'Funghi' or 'Dorad', they spent at least £1 million in the area.

Dolphin and whale watching has become an international activity of considerable economic and educational importance, as well as giving many scientists opportunities to pursue their research. Long-term photo-ID studies of bottle-nosed dolphins, killer whales (and humpbacks) in North America depend upon willing volunteers from the public. In the United Kingdom, well over a thousand people contribute to a national sightings scheme run by the Sea Watch Foundation, and help monitor coastal populations and the conservation threats they face. In 1992, a worldwide review of whale (and dolphin)-watching indicated that thirty countries were involved, and were receiving significant commercial revenue from it. At least four million people per year were engaged in this pursuit, spending at least £43.9 million a year.

Changes in group membership within a bottle-nosed dolphin herd during an 18-month period.

month	O	N	D	J	F	M	A	M	J	J	A	S	O	N	D	J	F	M
dolphin 1	●	●	●	●	●	●	●	●	●	●	●	●	●	●	●	●	●	●
2	●	●	●	●	●	●	●	●	●	●	●	●	●	●	●	●	●	●
3	●	●	●	●	●	●	●	●	●	●	●	●	●	●	●	●	●	●
4	●	●	●	○	○	●	●	●	●	●	●	●	●	●	●	●	●	●
(calf of 4) 4A	●	●	●	○	○	●	●	●	●	●	●	●	●	●	●	●	●	●
5	●	●	●	●	●	○	○	○	○	○	○	○	●	●	●	●	●	●
6	●	●	●	●	●	●	●	●	●	●	●	●	○	○	○	○	○	○
7	●	●	●	●	●	●	●	●	●	●	●	●	○	○	○	○	○	○
8	●	●	●	○	○	●	●	●	●	●	●	●	○	○	○	○	○	○
9	●	○	●	●	●	●	●	●	●	●	●	●	○	○	○	○	○	○
10	●	○	●	●	●	●	●	●	●	●	●	●	○	○	○	○	○	○
11	●	○	●	○	○	●	●	●	●	●	●	●	○	○	○	○	○	○
12	●	●	●	○	○	●	●	○	○	○	○	○	○	○	○	○	○	○
13	○	○	○	○	○	○	○	○	○	○	○	○	●	●	●	●	●	●
14	○	○	○	○	○	○	○	○	○	○	○	○	●	●	●	●	●	●
15	○	○	○	○	○	○	○	○	○	○	○	○	●	●	●	●	●	●
16	○	○	○	○	○	○	○	○	○	○	○	○	●	●	●	●	●	●
17	○	○	○	○	○	○	○	○	○	○	○	○	●	●	●	●	●	●
18	○	○	○	○	○	○	○	○	○	○	○	○	●	○	○	●	○	○

Dolphins are definitely in the public eye, but that alone does not guarantee their safety. Indeed, the tremendous interest and commercial potential in watching dolphins and whales can impose considerable pressure upon them through harassment and habitat degradation. Let us hope that the next century brings a maturing to the relationship between humans and dolphins so that that each can live in harmony with the other.

Further information

Publications

Bonner, Nigel, *Whales of the World* (Cassell, London, 1989). A good introduction to whales and dolphins, their natural history, biology and exploitation. Illustrated with line drawings, figures and colour photographs.

Carwardine, Mark, *Whales, Dolphins and Porpoises* (Dorling Kindersley, London, 1992). A children's guide to various topics about the lives of whales and dolphins. Lots of facts and colour paintings.

Cochrane, Amanda, and Karena Callen, *Dolphins and their power to heal* (Bloomsbury Press, London, 1992). An excursion into the unique relationship between dolphins and humans, and examination of the role they could play in healing human ailments. Illustrated with colour photographs.

The Encyclopaedia of Mammals, ed. David Macdonald (Unwin Hyman, London, 1989). Selected natural history accounts of cetaceans, written by a panel of spcialists. Beautifully illustrated with colour photographs, paintings, maps and figures.

Evans, Peter, *Guide to Identification of Cetaceans in the North-east Atlantic* (The Mammal Society, London, 1982). A short guide to all cetacean species occurring in the north-east Atlantic and how to identify them. Illustrated with line drawings.

Evans, Peter, *The Natural History of Whales and Dolphins* (Academic Press, London, 1987). A comprehensive review of the ecology, biology and conservation of the world's cetaceans. Chapters also on identification and where to see particular species around the world. Illustrated with colour photographs, line drawings, maps and figures.

The Handbook of British Mammals, ed. Gordon Corbet and Stephen Harris (Blackwell, Oxford, 1990). The definitive reference book to the mammal fauna of the British Isles. Includes a major section on British and Irish cetaceans, synthesising our recent knowledge of their status, distribution, biology and ecology.

Hoyt, Erich, *The Whale Watcher's Handbook* (Doubleday, New York, 1984). A guide to where to watch whales, but with particular emphasis on North America.

Klinowska, M., *Dolphins, Porpoises and Whales of the World. The IUCN Red Data Book* (IUCN, Gland, 1990). A comprehensive and systematic reference book to all the world's cetacean species with particular emphasis upon population biology and conservation threats. Illustrated with maps for selected species.

Leatherwood, Stephen, and Randall Reeves, *The Sierra Club Handbook of Whales and Dolphins* (Sierra Club Books, San Francisco, 1983). A pocket-sized illustrated guide to whales and dolphins throughout the world. The best identification guide currently available.

Papastavrou, Vassili, *Whale* (Dorling Kindersley, London, 1993). One in a series of educational eyewitness guides giving a range of facts about marine mammals (including dolphins) supported by lots of colour photographs and paintings.

Whales and Dolphins, ed. Tony Martin (Salamander Books, London, 1990) A beautifully illustrated systematic guide to whales and dolphins of the world with introductory sections on aspects of their biology.

Whales, Dolphins and Porpoises, ed. Richard Harrison (Merehurst, London, 1988). Authoritative accounts of various specific topics of interest to cetacean enthusiasts. Very fine illustrations.

Williams, Heathcote, *Falling for a Dolphin* (Jonathan Cape, London, 1990) A poem with pictures about the friendly dolphin (Funghi) in Co. Kerry which has given so many people pleasure since 1987. Abundantly illustrated with colour photographs.

Organizations to join

ORGANIZATIONS IN UNITED KINGDOM
Greenpeace
30-31 Islington Green, London N1 8XE
Campaigns against abuses of the environment using non-violent direct actions. Currently engaged in heightening public awareness of conservation threats to European cetaceans and campaigning for tighter legislation for their protection.

International Dolphin Watch
Director: Dr Horace Dobbs, Dolphin, Parklands, North Ferriby, Humberside HU14 3ET.
Concerned with man's relationship with dolphins, and ways to protect them from he adverse effects of hunan activities. Produces a regular newsletter *Dolphin*.

Sea Watch Foundation (formerly Mammal Society Cetacean Group)
Head of Research: Dr Peter Evans; Head of Administration: Paul Vodden, 7 Andrews Lane, Southwater, West Sussex RH13 7DY.
Maintains a national observer network and regional groups to monitor cetaceans and their conservation threats, particularly by both opportunistic and systematic recording of sightings. Produces a newsletter three times a year, occasional publications summarising results of research projects, a species identification guide, chart and slide training pack.

Whale and Dolphin Conservation Society
Director: Sean Whyte, Alexander House, James Street West, Bath, Avon BA1 2BT.
Devoted to the conservation and welfare of cetaceans, with particular emphasis upon public education. Produces a regular newsletter *Sonar*, and excellent reviews of special topics in an occasional publication *International Whale Bulletin*.

ORGANIZATIONS OUTSIDE THE UNITED KINGDOM

American Cetacean Society
P.O. Box 2639, San Pedro, CA 90731, USA.
Educates people about cetaceans and the need for their conservation. Produces regular newsletter *Whalewatcher* four times a year. Runs whale watching trips and holds biennial conferences.

Cetacean Society International
190 Stillwold Drive, Wethersfield, Connecticut 06109, USA.
Concerned with education and action related to cetacean conservation issues. Uses volunteers. Produces regular newsletter.

Dolphin Action and Protection Group
PO Box 2227, Fish Hoek 7975, South Africa.
Concerned with conservation of cetaceans in South Africa. Membership numbers restricted.

European Cetacean Society
Secretary: Dr Finn Larsen, c/o Greenland Fisheries Research Institute, Tagensvej 135, Copenhagen N, Denmark
Society bringing together amateurs and professionals interested in, or actively working on European cetaceans and their conservation. Produces regular newsletter three times a year, an annual report of the proceedings of the society's conference 'European Research on Cetaceans', and reports from workshops on special topics.

Long Term Research Institute
191 Weston Road, Lincoln, Massachusetts IL 01773, USA.
Research organization founded by Dr. Pobert Payne, particularly devoted to long term studies of cetaceans in the wild (mainly humpback and right whales).

Moclips Cetological Society
PO Box 945, Friday Harbour, WA 98250, USA.
Organization comprising the Whale Museum, Whale Research Laboratory, Whale School and Whale Hotline (the latter a free telephone service reporting cetacean sightings in western Washington). Produces journal *Cetus* twice a year, and other publications.

North Atlantic Marine Mammal Association
c/o Center for Coastal Studies, 59 Commercial Street, Provincetown Massachusetts IL 02659, USA.
Research, education and advisory organization specializing particularly in the study of humpbacks, right and fin whales off the eastern coast of the United States. Produces regular newsletters.

Oceanic Society
Fort Mason Centre, Building E, San Francisco CA 94123 USA.
Research, education and conservation of marine life. Offers whale watching trips. Produces magazine *Oceans* six times a year.

ORRCA
PO Box E293, St James NSW 2000, Australia.
Concerned with rescue and rehabilitation of beached cetaceans in Australia. Produces a regular newsletter.

Pacific Whale Foundation
Kealia Beach Plaza, 101 North Kihei Road, Hawaii HI 96753, USA.
Research organization, mainly studying humpbacks but also concerned with other cetaceans in the Pacific. Produces regular newsletter.

Project Interlock
Box 20, Whangarei, New Zealand.
Attempts to establish worldwide contact with humans and dolphins. Produces regular newsletter.

Society for Marine Mammalogy
Secretary: Dr Jim Harvey, Moss Landing Marine Laboratories, Moss Landing, CA 95039, USA.
American-based society concerned with the study and conservation of cetaceans around the world. Produces a journal *Marine Mammal Science* four times a year, and holds biennial conferences.

West Coast Whale Research Foundation
2020-1040 West Georgia Street, Vancouver BC V6E 4HI, Canada.
Concerned with research on various cetacean species along the west coast of Canada. Produces regular newsletter.

Whale Center
3929 Piedmont Avenue, Oakland CA 94611, USA.
An organization devoted to education, research and conservation of cetaceans. Currently concerned with drift net and entanglement issues. Produces a regular newsletter.

Whale Protection Fund
Center for Marine Education, 624 9th Street, Washington DC 20001, USA.
Originally founded to campaign against whaling, now also concerned with better protective legislation and habitat conservation. Produces a regular newsletter.

Index

Page references in bold type refer to illustrations

If you have enjoyed this book, you might be interested in other natural history titles we publish; they are avilable from bookshops or direct from us at 18 Anley Road, London W14 OBY. All are priced at £7.99 except where indicated, and all are illustrated with line drawings throughout. Please add £1 p & p when ordering direct:

World WIldlife Series

BIG CATS
Douglas Richardson
(£9.99)

CHIMPANZEES
Tess Lemmon

PARROTS
David Alderton
£9.99)

PENGUINS
John A. Love

SEA OTTERS
John A. Love
(£9.99)

SPIDERS
Michael Chinery

British Natural History Series

BADGERS
Michael Clark

BATS
Phil Richardson

DEER
Norma Chapman

EAGLES
John A. Love

FALCONS
Andrew VIllage

FROGS AND TOADS
Trevor Beebee

GARDEN CREEPY-CRAWLIES
Michael Chinery

HEDGEHOGS
Pat Morris

MICE AND VOLES
John Flowerdew

OTTERS
Paul Chanin

OWLS
Chris Mead

POND LIFE
Trevor Beebee

PONIES IN THE WILD
Elaine Gill

PUFFINS
Kenny Taylor

RABBITS AND HARES
Anne McBride

ROBINS
Chris Mead

SEALS
Sheila Anderson

SNAKES AND LIZARDS
Tom Langton

SQUIRRELS
Jessica Holm

STOATS AND WEASELS
Paddy Sleeman

URBAN FOXES
Stephen Harris

WHALES
Peter Evans

WILDCATS
Mike Tomkies